Gilbert **Delahaye** ◆ Marcel **Marlier**

martine
petit rat de l'opéra

casterman

Martine

Joyeuse et curieuse, Martine adore s'amuser avec ses amis et son petit chien Patapouf. Ensemble, ils découvrent le monde et vivent de véritables aventures. Une chose est sûre : avec Martine, on ne s'ennuie jamais !

Katia

Katia est la maîtresse de danse de Martine. C'est une ancienne danseuse étoile, et Martine l'admire beaucoup !

Patapouf

Ce petit chien est un vrai clown ! Il fait parfois des bêtises… mais il est si mignon que Martine lui pardonne toujours !

Moustache

Moustache est un petit chat malicieux et coquin. Très curieux, il furète partout. Mais il ne refuse jamais un câlin. Heureusement, Patapouf et lui sont bons amis et ne s'entendent pas « comme chien et chat ».

Tous les mercredis après-midi, Martine va à l'école
de danse. Elle y retrouve ses copines, mais aussi
Katia, leur professeur. C'est une ancienne danseuse
étoile, et Martine l'admire beaucoup !
Dès le premier jour, Katia a annoncé aux élèves :
– Si vous travaillez bien, nous présenterons
un spectacle à la fin de l'année !

Les leçons commencent toujours par des exercices
à la barre. Martine et ses amies apprennent à tenir
sur une jambe, le bras levé.
– Les doigts souples ! dit Katia. Dressez-vous
sur la pointe du pied, et restez bien droites !

– La première chose qu'une jeune danseuse doit connaître, explique Katia, ce sont les cinq positions. C'est pourquoi je vous les apprends dès la rentrée.

– Moi, je m'y entraîne tous les jours à la maison, dit Martine.

– Bravo ! Si tu faisais une démonstration à toute la classe ?

Martine fait tous les mouvements à la perfection !

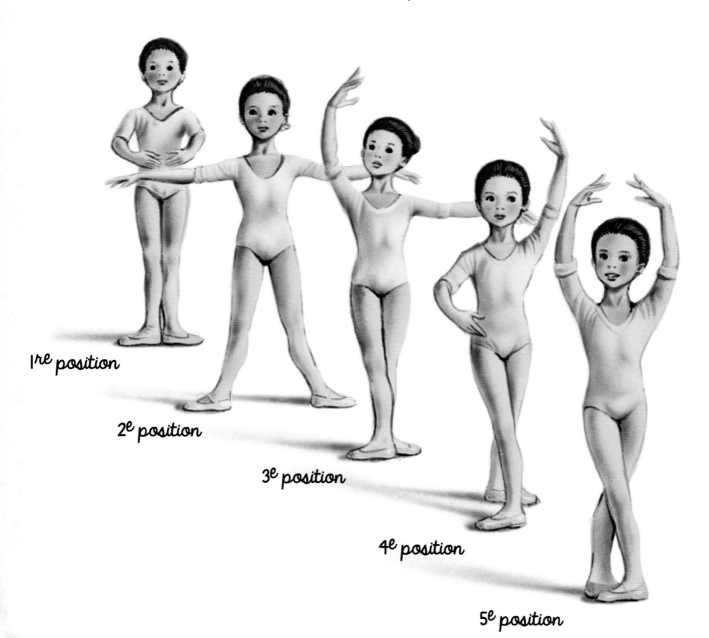

1re position

2e position

3e position

4e position

5e position

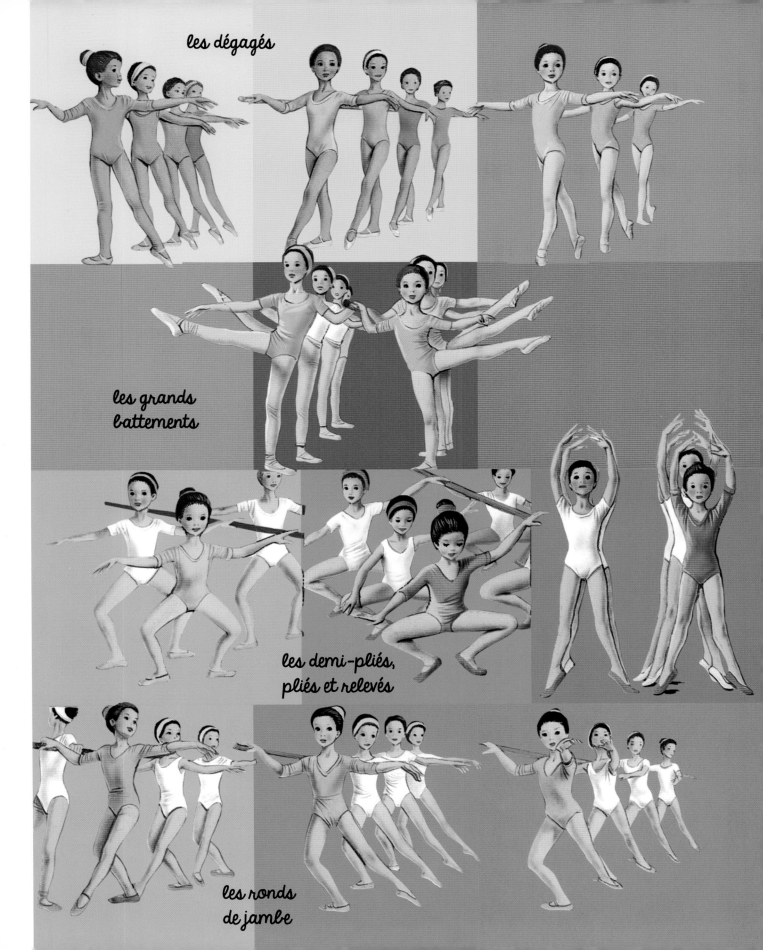

les dégagés

les grands
battements

les demi-pliés,
pliés et relevés

les ronds
de jambe

Dans la salle de danse, il y a un grand miroir qui permet de voir
si on fait les mouvements correctement.
Martine est en premier. Elle vérifie que son buste reste droit...
même quand elle se dresse sur la pointe du pied !
« Pointe tendue, bras souple, menton haut ! » répète Katia.

– Et n'oubliez pas de sourire, rappelle Sophie,
la pianiste. Quand vous serez sur scène,
le public voudra voir des visages joyeux !
« Facile, avec une mélodie aussi entraînante »,
pense Martine.

En plus, Moustache a le droit d'assister
aux leçons, et il observe les danseuses avec
tellement d'attention… Ça ne peut que donner
le sourire !

À chaque leçon, les élèves travaillent les arabesques.

Martine se cambre autant que possible.

«Sans forcer! pense-t-elle. Sinon, on risque de se blesser.»

Moustache tente d'imiter sa petite maîtresse… sauf qu'il a choisi
une position beaucoup moins difficile!

Heureusement, Katia est là pour aider chacune de ses élèves.

– Étire bien ta jambe, Martine. Le plus haut possible et la pointe tendue.

Une fois qu'elles se sont assouplies, les danseuses se mettent à la barre pour faire un « pied dans la main ». Il faut tenir cinq secondes !

grand battement
en attitude

Même les «grandes» du cours de danse moderne sont impressionnées par Martine et ses amies.

«Avec tout ce monde qui nous regarde, pense Martine, on se croirait déjà en plein spectacle!»

La figure préférée de Martine, c'est le grand écart. Elle le maîtrise parfaitement, comme ses copines.

– Chacune avec un port de bras différent! demande Katia. Julie, les bras en couronne, buste en avant! Martine, un bras relevé, tête en arrière!

port de bras
en grand écart

Les ballerines apprennent
la chorégraphie qu'elles
présenteront le jour du
spectacle. Elles écoutent
attentivement les consignes
de Katia :
– Vous devrez danser en
rythme, en gardant le regard
droit et le menton haut.
Martine, c'est toi qui
donneras la cadence,
les autres te suivront.

Martine est tellement fière !
Katia lui a donné le rôle
le plus important !
« Tout le monde compte
sur moi ! » pense-t-elle.

À chaque cours, les élèves révisent l'enchaînement avec grâce :
mouvements d'adage, arabesques…
Plus elles s'entraînent, plus elles progressent !

– Vous avez toutes atteint un très bon niveau,
dit Katia à ses élèves. Il est temps de passer
aux chaussons à pointe !
– Les pointes ? répète Martine. Comme les vraies
ballerines ?
– Oui, je vais vous montrer comment les utiliser.

Les filles enfilent leurs nouveaux chaussons. Elles ont
l'impression d'être des danseuses étoiles, comme Katia !

Pour s'habituer aux pointes, il faut commencer par des figures simples.

Martine essaye de faire un tour piqué.

– Bravo ! la félicite Katia. Maintenant, nous allons répéter

la chorégraphie du spectacle.

Les élèves dansent à merveille. C'est un sans-faute !

entrechat quatre

pas de bourrée

glissade grand jeté

ports de bras

Great Explorations in Math and Science (GEMS)

Lawrence Hall of Science,
University of California, Berkeley

SPACE SCIENCE SEQUENCE FOR GRADES 3–5

Unit 4 Moon Phases and Eclipses

The Space Science Sequence is a collaboration between the
Great Explorations in Math and Science (GEMS) Program
of the Lawrence Hall of Science,
University of California at Berkeley and the
NASA Sun–Earth Connection Education Forum
NASA Kepler Mission Education and Public Outreach
NASA Origins Education Forum/Hubble Space Telescope
NASA Solar System Education Forum
NASA IBEX Mission Education and Public Outreach
Special advisors: Cary Sneider and Timothy Slater
Foreword by Andrew Fraknoi

National Aeronautics and Space Administration
Funding for the GEMS Space Science Sequence was provided by the
NASA Forums and Missions listed on the title page.

Great Explorations in Math and Science (GEMS) is an ongoing curriculum development program and growing professional development network. There are more than 70 teacher's guides and handbooks in the GEMS Series, with materials kits available from Carolina Biological. GEMS is a program of the Lawrence Hall of Science, the public science education center of the University of California at Berkeley.

Lawrence Hall of Science
University of California
Berkeley, CA 94720-5200
Director: Elizabeth K. Stage

Project Coordinator: Carolyn Willard
Lead Developers: Kevin Beals, Carolyn Willard
Development Team: Jacqueline Barber, Lauren Brodsky, John Erickson, Alan Gould, Greg Schultz
Principal Editor: Lincoln Bergman
Production Manager: Steven Dunphy
Student Readings: Kevin Beals, Ashley Chase
Assessment Development: Kristin Nagy Catz
Evaluation: Kristin Nagy Catz, Ann Barter
Technology Development: Alana Chan, Nicole Medina, Glenn Motowidlak, Darrell Porcello, Roger Vang

Cover Design: Sherry McAdams, Carolina Biological Supply Co.
Internal Design: Lisa Klofkorn, Carol Bevilaqua, Sarah Kessler
Illustrations: Lisa Haderlie Baker
Copy Editor: Kathy Kaiser

This book is part of the *GEMS Space Science Sequence for Grades 3–5.*
The sequence is printed in five volumes with the following titles:
Introduction, Science Background, Assessment Scoring Guides
Unit 1: *How Big and How Far?*
Unit 2: *Earth's Shape and Gravity*
Unit 3: *How Does the Earth Move?*
Unit 4: *Moon Phases and Eclipses*

Published by Carolina Biological Supply Company. 2700 York Road, Burlington, NC 27215.
Call toll-free 1-800-334-5551.

Printed on recycled paper with soy-based inks.

ISBN 978-0-89278-334-2

UNIT 4
MOON PHASES AND ECLIPSES

UNIT 4
Moon Phases and Eclipses

SESSION SUMMARIES (4 Sessions)

4.1 Observing the Moon

Important scheduling note: Session 4.1 is composed of one 40-minute class session, plus a series of three to six trips outdoors to observe the Moon during the day. The Moon observations can be done before you present Unit 4, or between Sessions 4.1 and 4.2. Information about scheduling daytime observations and the alternatives is outlined in the Time Frame *and* Getting Ready *sections of Session 4.1.*

The session begins with the students filling out the *Pre–Unit 4 Questionnaire* to find out their ideas about Moon phases and eclipses. Next, students engage in a short activity about light and shadow, in which they discover that shadows are the absence of light, and that shadows can be thought of as having three parts. This knowledge will help them understand the reasons for Moon phases and eclipses, presented in later sessions.

Students learn how to use their fists to measure the Moon's position in the sky relative to the Sun. On three to six days during a ten-day period, students go outside to observe and measure the Moon's apparent position and shape. Through their observations, students notice a pattern which prepares them to understand the model for Moon phases that will be presented later in the unit.

4.2 Finding the Patterns in Moon Observations

This session gives students a chance to review and discuss the Moon observations they have made and generate a list of patterns they have discovered. They learn that the Moon changes its phase in a cycle that lasts about a month, and they learn the terms for the different phases.

As they discuss the evidence from their observations, students note a correlation between the Moon's phase and its apparent distance from the Sun. They also notice that the curved, outer edge of the Moon's shape always faces toward the Sun. These observations and the discussion in this session prepare students to understand the model they will use in Session 4.3 to explain the lunar cycle.

The concepts of models and evidence are introduced, and are added to the class concept wall.

4.3 Understanding Moon Phases

This session begins with a review of the student observations of the Moon. Why does the Moon appear to change shape when it is actually always spherical? To answer the question, students use a model to explain the Moon's monthly cycle of phases. In the model, students form a circle, standing around a light bulb "Sun." Each student's head represents the Earth. They hold "moon balls" in their outstretched hands and are able to observe Moon phases from an Earth perspective. Five key concepts about the Moon are added to the class concept wall.

In an evidence circle activity, students are challenged to debate which of two explanations on the *Moon Phases Explanations* sheet is best. In groups of four, they attempt to agree on the best explanation, using evidence from the moon ball model, from the *Shadow Play* activity in Session 4.1, and from their Moon observations. After the evidence circle discussion, students individually fill out the *Moon Phases Explanations* sheet, which serves as an embedded assessment of their understanding of Moon phases.

4.4 Understanding Eclipses of the Moon and Sun

Before moving on to model lunar and solar eclipses, students gather a bit more evidence to support the scientific model of Moon phases.

They begin by predicting the shape of several mystery objects placed on the overhead projector. The objects are hidden from view, but students are able to see the shadows that the objects cast. They learn that an object's shadow can provide evidence of its shape, although it's difficult to determine whether the object is two- or three-dimensional.

Next, they study photos of the Moon and conclude that a round Earth could not make a straight-edged shadow, such as the one seen in the Moon's quarter phase.

Having established that Moon phases are not caused by Earth's shadow, students now focus on celestial events that *are* caused by Earth's shadow—eclipses of the Moon. Returning to the moon ball model, they gather around a light bulb to simulate an eclipse of the Moon. Then they simulate an eclipse of the Sun.

These concepts are reviewed and applied to the real world as the students are shown photographs of actual eclipses of the Moon and Sun. The last two key concepts are added to the concept wall. Finally, students apply their knowledge as they draw an eclipse of the Moon and one of the Sun in *Eclipse Pamphlets.*

4.5 Impossible Missions

The session begins with a student reading titled *Eclipse Chaser!* which reviews the concepts presented in Session 4.4. Then, in the *Impossible Missions* activity, the class encounters four humorous statements describing missions to the Moon and the Sun. Each statement contains inaccuracies, which should be apparent to students who have a good grasp of the concepts addressed in Unit 4. Students work in evidence circles to discuss what's wrong with each statement and record their evidence-based explanations. At the end of Session 4.5, students fill out the *Post–Unit 4 Questionnaire* to assess what they have learned and how their ideas have changed.

This final session in the *Space Science Sequence* gives students a chance to review and apply concepts that they have learned in Unit 4. Teachers whose classes have experienced more than one unit in the sequence may select some *Additional Impossible Missions* to encourage students to revisit the concepts in other units.

Unit Goals

The Earth and Moon move with regular and predictable motion.

The relationship between the Earth, Moon, and Sun can be seen as a system.

A shadow is a 3–D area where light is blocked by an object.

The Moon's phases change from day to day in a cycle that lasts about a month.

Our changing view of sunlight shining on the Moon is what makes the Moon seem to change shape.

A solar eclipse occurs when the Moon blocks sunlight from reaching the Earth.

A lunar eclipse occurs when the Earth blocks sunlight from reaching the Moon.

Overview

Important scheduling note: Session 4.1 is composed of one 40-minute session, plus a series of three to six trips outdoors to observe the Moon during the day. Plan ahead for the observations, keeping the lunar cycle in mind. If possible, observations should be done during the school day. If this is not possible, there are two alternatives for observing the Moon: evening observations for homework, or observations using a simulation on the CD-ROM. Information about scheduling daytime observations and these alternatives is outlined in the Time Frame *and* Getting Ready *sections.*

The session begins with the students filling out the *Pre–Unit 4 Questionnaire* to find out their ideas about both phases and eclipses. The same questions will be asked in a *Post–Unit 4 Questionnaire* at the end of Session 4.5 to assess how much they have learned.

Next, students engage in a short activity about light and shadow, to help them understand the reasons for Moon phases and eclipses presented in later sessions. In teams of two, they explore shadows cast by a polystyrene ball and record their observations. As they share their observations with the class, they learn that shadows are the absence of light, and that shadows can be thought of as having three parts. After the discussion, four key concepts about shadows are posted on a concept wall that will be added to throughout the unit.

Students learn a way to measure the Moon's position in the sky relative to the Sun, using their fists. On three to six days during a ten-day period, students go outside to observe and measure the Moon's apparent position and shape. Through their observations, students notice a pattern, which prepares them to understand the model for Moon phases that will be presented later in the unit.

TEACHER CONSIDERATIONS

TEACHING NOTES

See page 481 at the end of this unit to see what your complete concept wall will look like.

Key Vocabulary

Science and Inquiry Vocabulary

Evidence

Scientific Explanation

Model

System

Prediction

Scientist

Scale Model

Three–Dimensional (3–D)

Two–Dimensional (2–D)

Space Science Vocabulary

Crescent Moon

Cycle

Diameter

Solar Eclipse (eclipse of the Sun)

Lunar Eclipse (eclipse of the Moon)

Full Moon

Gibbous

New Moon

Orbit

Phase

Quarter Moon

Satellite

Shadow

Sphere

Rotate

Revolve

Time Frame: This time frame has a regular class session, and several associated short sessions when students do the outdoor observations of the Moon. All the Moon observations should be completed by the time you begin Session 4.2. You could do the observations any time before the first class session, or schedule them between Sessions 4.1 and 4.2.

Observing the Moon	Estimated Time
Taking the *Pre–Unit 4 Questionnaire*	15 minutes
Shadow Play	15 minutes
Shadow talk	10 minutes
TOTAL	**40 minutes**

Observing the Moon and measuring with fists	Four to six 15-minute observations
Summarizing class data from Moon observations	15 minutes
TOTAL FOR OBSERVATIONS	**75 to 105 minutes**

What You Need

Unit Goals

The Earth and Moon move with regular and predictable motion.

The relationship between the Earth, Moon, and Sun can be seen as a system.

A shadow is a 3–D area where light is blocked by an object.

The Moon's phases change from day to day in a cycle that lasts about a month.

Our changing view of sunlight shining on the Moon is what makes the Moon seem to change shape.

A solar eclipse occurs when the Moon blocks sunlight from reaching the Earth.

A lunar eclipse occurs when the Earth blocks sunlight from reaching the Moon.

For the class
- ❑ a calendar, newspaper, or website to look up the date of the next full Moon
- ❑ 1 large sheet of butcher paper
- ❑ wide-tip felt pen or crayon
- ❑ sentence strips for 4 key concepts
- ❑ 1 lamp with no shade
- ❑ 1 25-foot extension cord
- ❑ 1 40-watt clear light bulb
- ❑ 1 75-watt clear light bulb
- ❑ duct tape or masking tape for taping down cords
- ❑ overhead projector and screen
- ❑ *Shadow Play* overhead transparency, from the transparency packet
- ❑ overhead projector
- ❑ *Optional:* Moon Phase interactive on CD–ROM and projector

TEACHER CONSIDERATIONS

CD-ROM NOTES

Observing Moon Phases, *this series of images can serve as an option if students can't observe the real Moon in the sky:* Witness the changes of the phases of the Moon over four evenings at sunset. Click the "back" and "next" buttons to scroll through the chronological sequence of sunset images with various moon phases. Students can measure how many finger widths fit between the setting Sun and the Moon on each evening. The Moon's phase changes slightly in each image, from a thin to a fatter crescent. The sunset images were all shot at the Lawrence Hall of Science from the same position over the course of a week. Further instructions for using this program are included on the CD-ROM.

Another strategy to try if weather or other conditions preclude direct observations of the Moon is to use the Powerpoint file: "Simulated Moon Phase Observations" that can be found on the NASA Kepler Mission website, http://kepler.nasa.gov/ed/SimMoon.html Instructions for how to use the simulation with your class can be found on that web page.

Key Vocabulary

Science and Inquiry Vocabulary

Evidence

Scientific Explanation

Model

System

Prediction

Scientist

Scale Model

Three–Dimensional (3–D)

Two–Dimensional (2–D)

Space Science Vocabulary

Crescent Moon

Cycle

Diameter

Solar Eclipse (eclipse of the Sun)

Lunar Eclipse (eclipse of the Moon)

Full Moon

Gibbous

New Moon

Orbit

Phase

Quarter Moon

Satellite

Shadow

Sphere

Rotate

Revolve

For each team of two students
- ❑ 1 2-inch polystyrene sphere*
- ❑ 1 bottle cap (any kind in a size that will work as a stand for the polystyrene sphere)
- ❑ 1 piece of white paper; standard 8½" x 11" is fine, but larger paper is better

Note: Polystyrene spheres may be purchased inexpensively from a number of sources, including Carolina Biological. The ones in the Carolina materials kit come with a pre punched hole, into which students can put a pencil to serve as a holder. Other balls will also work if they are white (or light) in color and opaque. Styrofoam balls can be used, but as they aren't as opaque or reflective as polystyrene, they won't work as well.

For each student
- ❑ *Pre–Unit 4 Questionnaire* from the student sheet packet
- ❑ *Shadow Play* student sheet from the student sheet packet
- ❑ 3 to 8 sheets of scratch paper
- ❑ 1 manila folder
- ❑ pencil

Getting Ready Before the Day of the Activity

Plan How You Will Schedule the Moon Observations

1. Plan for students to observe the Moon. During about half of each month, the Moon is visible in the daytime. During the other half of the month, it is visible in the evening. If at all possible, we recommend taking your class outside for daytime Moon observations three to six times, using the scheduling information that follows.

Best of all would be to have students observe the Moon over a full month, making daytime observations with the whole class during one part of the month and evening observations as homework for the other part.

Unit Goals

The Earth and Moon move with regular and predictable motion.

The relationship between the Earth, Moon, and Sun can be seen as a system.

A shadow is a 3–D area where light is blocked by an object.

The Moon's phases change from day to day in a cycle that lasts about a month.

Our changing view of sunlight shining on the Moon is what makes the Moon seem to change shape.

A solar eclipse occurs when the Moon blocks sunlight from reaching the Earth.

A lunar eclipse occurs when the Earth blocks sunlight from reaching the Moon.

TEACHER CONSIDERATIONS

TEACHING NOTES

Tips for Leading Good Discussions: Engaging students in thoughtful discussions is a powerful way to enrich their learning. Even the most experienced teacher can use a few reminders about how to lead a good discussion. Listed below are some general strategies to keep in mind while leading a class discussion:

- Ask broad questions (questions which have many possible responses) to encourage participation.
- Use focused questions sparingly (questions which have only one correct response) to recall specific information.
- Use wait time (pause about 3 seconds after asking a question before calling on a student).
- Give non-judgmental responses, even to seemingly outlandish ideas.
- Listen to student responses respectfully, and ask what their evidence is for their explanations.
- Ask other students for alternative opinions or ideas.
- Try to create a safe, non-intimidating environment for discussion.
- Try to call on as many females as males.
- Try to include the whole group in the discussion.
- Offer "safe" questions to shy students.
- Employ hand raising or hand signals to insure whole group involvement.
- Take time to probe what students are thinking.
- Consider your role as a collaborator with the students, trying to figure things out together.
- Encourage students to figure things out for themselves, rather than telling them the answer.

What Some Teachers Said

"We were able to observe the Moon during the day for three days in a row. This was one of the highlights for the students. They loved going outdoors and being "scientists." This also made the unit meaningful to students."

"They were (and are) very engaged...They were very eager to help each other. They LOVE drawing and recording. This activity has been a topic for discussion all day for two days. The last thing many said on Friday was that they were eager to observe in the morning."

2. Two alternatives if daytime observations are not possible. It is best for students to make observations of the real Moon as a class. However, cloudy weather or other conditions may make daytime observations impossible. Weekends, vacation days, or school events can sometimes make scheduling a series of class observations of the Moon challenging. If you can't take your students outside to see the real Moon, there are two alternative ways of giving them a similar experience described on page 413:

  a. Assign evening Moon observations for homework.
  b. Use the *Moon Phases Simulation* on the CD-ROM.

Note: If you want to start your Moon observations before beginning Unit 4, use the section entitled Observing the Moon *and* Measuring with Fists *(page 426) in Session 4.1 of the guide to introduce the outdoor observations to students.*

Scheduling Daytime Moon Observations

1. **Useful knowledge.** Here are a few facts about the position of the Moon in the sky that will help you plan:

  a. The Moon, like the Sun, is visible for an average of 12 hours per day—sometimes longer, sometimes shorter.

  b. The Moon, like the Sun, rises from the eastern horizon and sets toward the western horizon. (The rising point is not necessarily due east; the setting point is not necessarily due west.)

  c. Because the Moon orbits the Earth, its position in the sky changes continuously. The Moon moves one full moon diameter every hour, 24 hours a day. Because of this orbital motion, the rising and setting times for the Moon change every day. It can rise and set at any time, day or night!

  d. The Moon rises and sets an average of 50 minutes *later* each day.

Unit Goals

The Earth and Moon move with regular and predictable motion.

The relationship between the Earth, Moon, and Sun can be seen as a system.

A shadow is a 3–D area where light is blocked by an object.

The Moon's phases change from day to day in a cycle that lasts about a month.

Our changing view of sunlight shining on the Moon is what makes the Moon seem to change shape.

A solar eclipse occurs when the Moon blocks sunlight from reaching the Earth.

A lunar eclipse occurs when the Earth blocks sunlight from reaching the Moon.

TEACHER CONSIDERATIONS

TEACHING NOTES—WHAT TO DO IF YOU HAVE TROUBLE SCHEDULING DAYTIME MOON OBSERVATIONS

If conditions make it impossible to take your class outdoors for a series of daytime Moon observations, choose one of the alternatives that follow. But we still recommend that the class go outside to observe the real Moon at least once, if possible.

Alternative I: Evening Moon Observations as Homework
Your students can observe the pattern of changing Moon phases and positions at sunset. The disadvantage is that there will probably be some students who miss the experience this way.

Two or three days after the new Moon phase, the Moon will appear as a thin crescent near the setting Sun in the evening. Check a calendar or newspaper to find out when the Moon will first become visible after the new Moon. Have students draw the Moon every evening at sunset when possible, marking the date and number of fists between the Sun and Moon, as outlined in the Session 4.1 activity. They need at least three or four observations on cloudless evenings to draw their conclusions.

Alternative II: Moon Phase Simulation on the CD-ROM
Note: The simulation gives students a sense of the pattern of Moon phases and positions that they would see in the real sky. However, in the simulation, the Moon's position relative to the Sun does not change as much each night as it does in the real sky. The simulation includes a sequence of only four nights because of the limitation of screen size and limitations of representing a three-dimensional sky in a two-dimensional format.

1. **Tell your students that they will be making Moon observations and measurements using a CD-ROM simulation.** The simulation will show what the sky looks like near the western horizon at sunset for four nights in a row. Project the first image on the screen. Point out where the Moon is in the image, and the point on the horizon where the Sun has just set.

continued on page 415

Key Vocabulary

Science and Inquiry Vocabulary

Evidence

Scientific Explanation

Model

System

Prediction

Scientist

Scale Model

Three–Dimensional (3–D)

Two–Dimensional (2–D)

Space Science Vocabulary

Crescent Moon

Cycle

Diameter

Solar Eclipse (eclipse of the Sun)

Lunar Eclipse (eclipse of the Moon)

Full Moon

Gibbous

New Moon

Orbit

Phase

Quarter Moon

Satellite

Shadow

Sphere

Rotate

Revolve

Unit Goals

The Earth and Moon move with regular and predictable motion.

The relationship between the Earth, Moon, and Sun can be seen as a system.

A shadow is a 3–D area where light is blocked by an object.

The Moon's phases change from day to day in a cycle that lasts about a month.

Our changing view of sunlight shining on the Moon is what makes the Moon seem to change shape.

A solar eclipse occurs when the Moon blocks sunlight from reaching the Earth.

A lunar eclipse occurs when the Earth blocks sunlight from reaching the Moon.

2. Check a newspaper or calendar to find out the date of the next full Moon. Also, find out the time of sunrise (within 15 or 20 minutes is fine). Now, make a quick calculation:

   a. When the Moon is full, it will set in the west just about when the Sun is rising in the east.

   b. One day later, the Moon will set about 50 minutes after sunrise.

   c. Two days later, the Moon will be higher in the sky and will set about one hour and 40 minutes (100 minutes) after sunrise.

   d. Three days later, the Moon will set about 2.5 hours (150 minutes) after sunrise.

   e. And so on…

3. If your class is going to observe the Moon during the early morning, you may only need to wait three or four days after the full Moon to start observing. If your class is going to take measurements in the afternoon, you will need to wait a greater number of days for the Moon to be visible when you go outside.

4. Moon observations do not have to be made at the same time every day. Students will measure the separation of the Sun and the Moon, not where they are in relation to the horizon.

5. Just before class on the day of the activity, go outdoors and find the Moon. Make sure that it is not obscured by clouds, trees, or buildings. If it is cloudy, plan to begin on the next clear day.

Getting Ready on the Day of the Class Session

1. Darken the room. If you can't darken your classroom completely, find a room for the *Shadow Play* activity that you can darken by drawing curtains or by taping black paper over the windows.

2. Place the lamp and light bulb in the center of the room. This should be at about the same level as student desks. Tape the cord down to the floor for safety.

3. Decide how to shift student desks for the *Shadow Play* activity. Each pair of students will set a polystyrene sphere on a base (bottle cap) on a desk or table. They will observe light and shadow on and around the sphere. To ensure that students don't block one another's light, you will probably need to have them move some desks so that they make a rough circle around the bulb.

TEACHER CONSIDERATIONS

TEACHING NOTES—WHAT TO DO IF YOU HAVE TROUBLE SCHEDULING DAYTIME MOON OBSERVATIONS, *CONTINUED*

2. **Have students stand or sit in a curved line when they make their observations, so that they are all the same distance from the screen.** This way, their measurements should be similar, and you can take a class average.

Why students should be the same distance from the screen: When using the fist measuring technique with the real Moon, everyone in the class is the same distance from the real Moon and Sun in the sky. When using the simulation, if students are seated at different distances from the screen, their measurements will vary depending on where they are in the classroom.

3. **Record observations and measurements of the simulated Moon for each "night."** Tell students to measure the distance between the spot where the Sun set and the Moon. (See directions in *Observing the Moon and Measuring with Fists.*) For the simulation, because of the size of the screen, they will use **a finger** instead of a fist. Tell them to measure the number of finger-widths between the Moon and the point where the Sun sets. Then they should draw the shape of the Moon on a piece of paper, and its position in relation to the Sun, as shown on the screen. Have each student write the number of finger-widths between the Sun and Moon below the drawing of the Moon.

Key Vocabulary

Science and Inquiry Vocabulary

Evidence

Scientific Explanation

Model

System

Prediction

Scientist

Scale Model

Three–Dimensional (3–D)

Two–Dimensional (2–D)

Space Science Vocabulary

Crescent Moon

Cycle

Diameter

Solar Eclipse (eclipse of the Sun)

Lunar Eclipse (eclipse of the Moon)

Full Moon

Gibbous

New Moon

Orbit

Phase

Quarter Moon

Satellite

Shadow

Sphere

Rotate

Revolve

Unit Goals

The Earth and Moon move with regular and predictable motion.

The relationship between the Earth, Moon, and Sun can be seen as a system.

A shadow is a 3–D area where light is blocked by an object.

The Moon's phases change from day to day in a cycle that lasts about a month.

Our changing view of sunlight shining on the Moon is what makes the Moon seem to change shape.

A solar eclipse occurs when the Moon blocks sunlight from reaching the Earth.

A lunar eclipse occurs when the Earth blocks sunlight from reaching the Moon.

4. **Determine which light bulb is best by placing one of them into the lamp and darkening the room.** Test a polystyrene sphere at about the same distance from the lamp as the students will. Observe the contrast between dark and light sides of the sphere, and the shadow it makes on the desk. If necessary, change the bulb and again observe the contrast.

5. **Make one copy for each student** of the *Pre–Unit 4 Questionnaire* and the *Shadow Play* sheet.

6. **Have on hand a piece of white paper, one polystyrene sphere, and one bottle cap** per pair of students.

7. **Make an overhead transparency** of *Shadow Play.*

8. **Arrange for an overhead projector** to display images to the class.

9. **Choose a wall or bulletin board that can serve as a "concept wall"** for Unit 4. This is where you will post sentence strips showing the key concepts learned. You'll post the strips in two columns. (Please see the illustration on page 481.) The left column should be titled *What We Have Learned About Evidence and Models.* The right column should be titled, *What We Have Learned About Space Science.* None of the key concepts about evidence and models will be posted until Session 4.2.

10. **Prepare sentence strips** for the following four key space science concepts introduced during this session. Have them ready to post during the session under the *What We Have Learned About Space Science* column.

A shadow is a dark area where light is blocked by an object.
Shadows are actually three-dimensional.
We can see the shadow cast by one object on another object.
The shadow begins on the dark side of the object that is blocking the light.

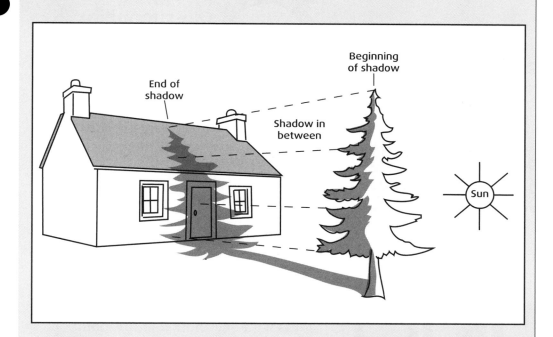

PRE–UNIT 4 QUESTIONNAIRE, PAGE 1

Session 4.1

Name_____

Pre–Unit 4 Questionnaire, page 1

1. Which picture below is *wrong*: A or B? (Circle one.) *Drawings are not to scale.*

It is wrong because. . . _____

_____

_____

_____

A
SUN   MOON

B
SUN   MOON

2. Here are some pictures of how the Moon looks at different times of the month.

Why does the Moon seem to change its shape during the month? (Circle A, B, C, or D.)
A. The Moon gets smaller and bigger.
B. Clouds block part of the Moon from our view.
C. The Earth's shadow covers part of the Moon.
D. We see the sunny side of the Moon from different directions.

(Over)

Pre–Unit 4 Questionnaire

1. Questionnaire about your ideas. Tell the class that they will be studying what causes the phases of the Moon, and what causes eclipses of the Sun and the Moon. Say that you want to find out their current ideas by having them each fill out a questionnaire.

2. Write your own ideas. Tell them that if they don't know an answer or what some of the words on the questionnaire mean, they should just put down their ideas anyway. Tell them that because the questionnaire is to find out what each of them is thinking, they should not share ideas with one another at this point. Assure them that this questionnaire will not affect their grades.

3. Administer the questionnaire. Hand out a copy of the questionnaire to each student. Have them write their names at the top of their papers and answer the questions.

4. Early finishers. You may want to tell students who finish early that they may either draw on the back of their questionnaire or read. Allow time for everyone to finish, and then collect the papers.

Shadow Play

1. Ask students about shadows. Ask students what they have observed about shadows, and allow a few minutes for them to share. Say that they are going to do a short activity to understand light and shadows better.

2. Pair students and shift desks if necessary. Assign student pairs and have them rearrange desks around the light bulb, as necessary. (Don't pass out the materials yet.)

PRE–UNIT 4 QUESTIONNAIRE, PAGE 2

TEACHING NOTES

Emphasize that students should read carefully and take their time: The questions are short but challenging. Remind students to think carefully about each answer and to read every word.

QUESTIONNAIRE CONNECTION

We have included *Questionnaire Connection* notes in later sessions of the unit to help you highlight when an activity or discussion relates to specific questions on the questionnaire. It is important to look over your students' questionnaires before getting too far into the unit, so you can identify areas that may need more or less instruction, and any major misconceptions that students have.

Scoring Guide for the *Pre–Unit 4 Questionnaire:* The questionnaire can be scored using the scoring guide on page 86.

Different Order of Questions on the Pre and Post Questionnaires: The *Post–Unit 4 Questionnaire* in Session 4.5 is identical in content to the *Pre–Unit 4 Questionnaire*, but the placement of some questions and the order of the possible answers is different. This is to encourage students to answer thoughtfully, rather than simply to remember the order of the answers.

Session 4.1

Pre–Unit 4 Questionnaire, page 2

Name_____

3. Why do we see an eclipse of the Sun? (Circle A, B, C, or D.) *Drawings are not to scale.*

A Clouds go in front of the Sun.	B The Moon goes between the Earth and the Sun.
C The Sun is between the Earth and the Moon.	D The Earth goes between the Moon and the Sun.

4. Why do we see an eclipse of the Moon? (Circle A, B, C, or D.) *Drawings are not to scale.*

A The Moon goes into the Earth's shadow.	B Clouds go in front of the Moon.
C The Moon goes between the Earth and the Sun.	D The Sun is between the Earth and the Moon.

SHADOW PLAY

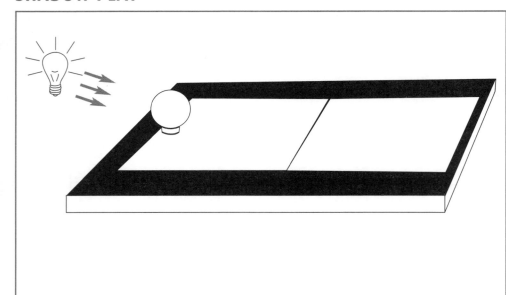

3. Demonstrate the activity. Turn on the light bulb. Explain that each pair of students will set a white piece of paper on their desk or table. Show how to set a polystyrene sphere on an upside-down bottle cap so that it will not roll. Set it at the end of the piece of paper closest to the light bulb. Caution students not to play with the spheres.

The white paper makes it easier to see shadows.

4. Point out parts of the shadow. Point out that there is a shadow cast by the sphere on the paper. Tell students that this is the part of a shadow that most people notice. Ask if anyone can identify *other parts* of the sphere's shadow. If they don't mention them, be sure to point out:

- The side of the sphere facing away from the light bulb, which is dark.

- The area *in the air* on the side of the sphere away from the light bulb. Draw their attention to this part of the shadow by putting your finger there and letting students see that it is in shadow. Point out that this part of the shadow can only be seen when you move an object into it.

5. *Shadow Play* tasks. Tell them that each student will fill out a *Shadow Play* sheet. Go over each step of the task:

- Put your finger into the shadow of the sphere.

- On your paper, shade in every place that the sphere makes dark on the paper, on itself, and in the air next to it.

- Label where it is light on the drawing of the sphere.

- Label where it is dark on the drawing of the sphere.

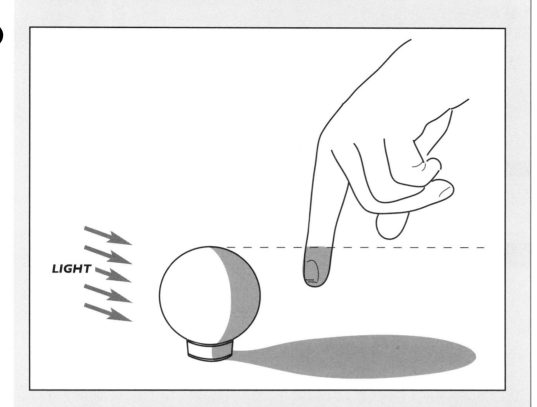

LIGHT

SHADOW PLAY OVERHEAD

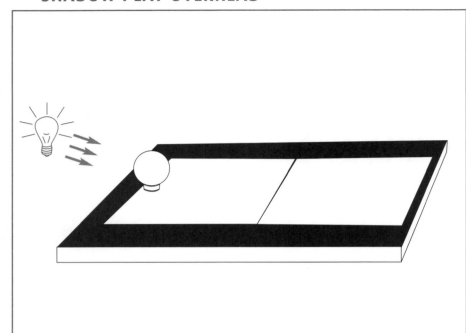

6. Distribute materials. Give a sphere, white paper, and bottle cap to each pair of students and a *Shadow Play* sheet and pencil to each student. Have them begin filling out the sheet.

Shadow Talk

1. Shadow discoveries. Collect the materials, except for the *Shadow Play* sheets, and have students return their desks to their original positions. Ask, "What did you discover about shadows?"

2. Record student ideas on *Shadow Play* overhead. Show the *Shadow Play* overhead transparency. As students share, either draw these ideas on the overhead transparency yourself, or ask students to come forward and draw them. After a student has shared where he or she drew the shadow, and it has been added to the class drawing, ask if other students noticed shadow anywhere else in the model that they can add.

There may be some disagreement about exactly how to draw or describe the shadow. This is okay: the objective is that students understand that there are three "parts" of the shadow, as described in number 5 below.

3. Light travels in straight lines. Shadow is the absence of light. Ask, "What is causing the shadow?" [The sphere is blocking the light from the light bulb.] Tell them that a shadow is not really a "thing." It's the absence of light in an area where the light is being blocked by an object.

4. A hand shadow is blocked light. Hold your hand out in front of the overhead projector (or the light bulb) to cast a shadow. Tell your students that light is shining in straight lines from the light bulb. Your hand blocks some of those rays of light. The light can't go around your hand.

TEACHER CONSIDERATIONS

TEACHING NOTES

Don't introduce phases and eclipses yet: The goal of the *Shadow Play* activity is to introduce some concepts about light and shadows that will help students later in the unit when they investigate the causes of Moon phases and of eclipses. However, some of your students may begin making discoveries during this first session about how light and shadow on the sphere seem to create phases or eclipses. If this happens, share their excitement, and tell them that they will be using the spheres again in later sessions to explore this further. Because most students need the guidance that is provided in later sessions, refrain from discussing phases or eclipses with the class now.

Key Vocabulary

Science and Inquiry Vocabulary

Evidence

Scientific Explanation

Model

System

Prediction

Scientist

Scale Model

Three–Dimensional (3–D)

Two–Dimensional (2–D)

Space Science Vocabulary

Crescent Moon

Cycle

Diameter

Solar Eclipse (eclipse of the Sun)

Lunar Eclipse (eclipse of the Moon)

Full Moon

Gibbous

New Moon

Orbit

Phase

Quarter Moon

Satellite

Shadow

Sphere

Rotate

Revolve

Unit Goals

The Earth and Moon move with regular and predictable motion.

The relationship between the Earth, Moon, and Sun can be seen as a system.

A shadow is a 3–D area where light is blocked by an object.

The Moon's phases change from day to day in a cycle that lasts about a month.

Our changing view of sunlight shining on the Moon is what makes the Moon seem to change shape.

A solar eclipse occurs when the Moon blocks sunlight from reaching the Earth.

A lunar eclipse occurs when the Earth blocks sunlight from reaching the Moon.

5. Three parts of a shadow. Tell them that shadows can be described as having three parts (demonstrate each of these with your hand, as well as with the drawing on the *Shadow Play* diagram):

• *The beginning of the shadow.* Point to the dark side of your hand. Say that just like the sphere, your hand is blocking the light. The dark side of your hand is part of its shadow. Your hand makes a shadow on itself.

• *The end of the shadow.* Point to the shadow shape that your hand casts on the wall.

• *The shadow in-between.* The "shadow in-between" starts with the dark side of your hand and goes all the way to the wall. You don't see this part of the shadow unless an object is put into it. Put something in your hand's shadow. A shadow is three–dimensional.

6. Introduce the concept wall and post key concepts about light and shadows. Say that they have made important observations. Post the four concepts about light and shadows on the concept wall. Read the concepts with the students, and say that they will be finding out more about light and shadows **in space** in the coming sessions. They will add concepts on this wall during the coming activities, and it will be a record of what they have learned.

A shadow is a dark area where light is blocked by an object.
Shadows are actually three-dimensional.
We can see the shadow cast by one object on another object.
The shadow begins on the dark side of the object that is blocking the light.

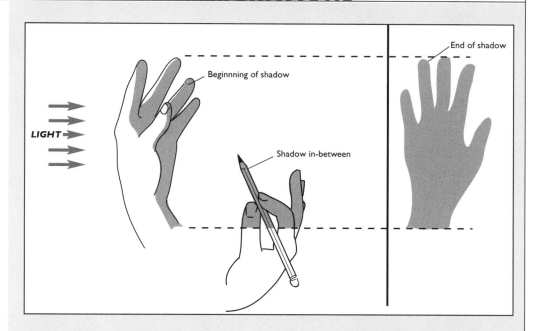

TEACHING NOTES

If necessary, review or define three-dimensional (3-D): Define
3–D as having three dimensions, such as height, width, and length. An
object that is two-dimensional (2-D) has only two dimensions, such as
length and width. A piece of paper is two–dimensional.

Observing the Moon and Measuring with Fists

1. Observing the Moon over two weeks. Say that they will be returning to the subject of shadows in later class sessions, but right now the class is about to begin observing the Moon.

2. Ask questions about the Moon. Ask a few questions about students' experiences in observing the Moon:
- Where have they seen the Moon in the sky?
- What did it look like?
- Did anyone see the Moon this morning?
- If yes, what shape was it?

3. Distribute materials and go outside. Say that they are going to observe the Moon several times over the next two weeks, and learn more about why it seems to change its shape. Provide each student with paper, pencil, and a manila folder (to use as a writing surface). Then, go outdoors and find the Moon!

4. Describe the Moon's shape and which side is facing the Sun. Gather the students where they can see the Sun and the Moon. Ask them to describe the shape of the Moon. Ask, "Does the side of the Moon that is curved outward like the edge of a ball face toward the Sun or away from the Sun?" [Toward the Sun.]

5. Students draw Sun and Moon. Ask students to draw the Sun and the Moon just as they appear in the sky. Give them time to complete their drawings. Have each student put their name and the date on the paper.

6. Measuring with fists. Show the students how to measure the distance between the Sun and Moon with fists, as follows:

a. Hold one hand over the Sun to shield your eyes. (Or stand in the shadow of a building so that the Sun is just barely hidden.) *Tell students not to look directly at the Sun, as it can be harmful to their eyes.*

b. Make the other hand into a fist, and hold your arm out straight.

c. Hold your fist so that the wide part points toward the Sun.

d. Move your fist toward the Moon one "fist-width" at a time, counting as you go. With practice, your students' measurements of the number of fists between the Sun and Moon will become more consistent. *A "fist-width" is across the knuckles.*

Unit Goals

The Earth and Moon move with regular and predictable motion.

The relationship between the Earth, Moon, and Sun can be seen as a system.

A shadow is a 3–D area where light is blocked by an object.

The Moon's phases change from day to day in a cycle that lasts about a month.

Our changing view of sunlight shining on the Moon is what makes the Moon seem to change shape.

A solar eclipse occurs when the Moon blocks sunlight from reaching the Earth.

A lunar eclipse occurs when the Earth blocks sunlight from reaching the Moon.

Key Vocabulary

**Science and
Inquiry Vocabulary**

Evidence

Scientific Explanation

Model

System

Prediction

Scientist

Scale Model

Three–Dimensional (3–D)

Two–Dimensional (2–D)

Space Science Vocabulary

Crescent Moon

Cycle

Diameter

Solar Eclipse (eclipse
of the Sun)

Lunar Eclipse (eclipse
of the Moon)

Full Moon

Gibbous

New Moon

Orbit

Phase

Quarter Moon

Satellite

Shadow

Sphere

Rotate

Revolve

Unit Goals

The Earth and Moon move with regular and predictable motion.

The relationship between the Earth, Moon, and Sun can be seen as a system.

A shadow is a 3–D area where light is blocked by an object.

The Moon's phases change from day to day in a cycle that lasts about a month.

Our changing view of sunlight shining on the Moon is what makes the Moon seem to change shape.

A solar eclipse occurs when the Moon blocks sunlight from reaching the Earth.

A lunar eclipse occurs when the Earth blocks sunlight from reaching the Moon.

7. Measure three or four times. Ask students to measure the distance between the Sun and the Moon three or four times, until they get about the same number of fists each time. Then, quickly poll the entire class to find out how many fists they measured. Help individuals whose measurements differ by more than three fists from the group average.

8. Write number of fists on drawing. Instruct each student to write the number of fists they measured next to their drawing of the Moon. Then, have them put their drawings into their folders.

Debriefing the Observations

1. Observe the Moon several more times during the following ten days. When possible, take your students outdoors to make a new drawing, on a new sheet of paper, of the Sun and Moon. Each drawing should show how the Sun and Moon appear in the sky, the distance between them in fists, and the date. If it is cloudy for a day or two, go out on the next clear day. A total of four or five measurements is adequate. Even three measurements taken whenever possible during the 10-day period will establish a pattern.

2. Discuss and make predictions after each measurement. After you return to the classroom following each observation, spend a few minutes discussing how the Moon has changed shape, and its distance from the Sun. Each time, ask students to notice which side is facing toward the Sun. [The curved side.] Ask students to predict what shape the Moon will be in two or three days, and how many fists from the Sun it will be.

3. Next session to summarize Moon observations. After about 10 days, the Moon will no longer be visible during the daytime. That is the time to do Session 4.2, in which all the observations will be summarized.

TEACHER CONSIDERATIONS

PROVIDING MORE EXPERIENCE

Drawing the Moon for a month: Give students a copy of a calendar page for the next month (the type of calendar with a large square for each day). Assign them to observe the Moon each day they can, and to draw the shape of the Moon in the appropriate square on the calendar. If the Moon is not visible, tell them to leave the day blank.

You might want to ask them to fill in the blank days through research on the Internet, in the newspapers, or using some other source.

TEACHING NOTES

Introducing key vocabulary: The word *phases*, as well as the terms *new, crescent, quarter, gibbous,* and *full,* will be formally introduced in the next class session. However, it's fine to introduce them now, if appropriate.

OPTIONAL PROMPTS FOR WRITING OR DISCUSSION

You may want to have students use one of the prompts that follow for science journal writing at the end of this session or as homework. The prompts could also be used for a discussion or during a final student sharing circle.

- What kinds of changes do you think you will observe as you watch the Moon over time?

- How would you describe shadows to a child who did not understand them at all?

- Draw an object, and draw a light bulb near it. Shade in where you think the shadows would be.

Key Vocabulary

Science and Inquiry Vocabulary

Evidence

Scientific Explanation

Model

System

Prediction

Scientist

Scale Model

Three–Dimensional (3–D)

Two–Dimensional (2–D)

Space Science Vocabulary

Crescent Moon

Cycle

Diameter

Solar Eclipse (eclipse of the Sun)

Lunar Eclipse (eclipse of the Moon)

Full Moon

Gibbous

New Moon

Orbit

Phase

Quarter Moon

Satellite

Shadow

Sphere

Rotate

Revolve

SESSION 4.2

Finding the Patterns in Moon Observations

Unit Goals

The Earth and Moon move with regular and predictable motion.

The relationship between the Earth, Moon, and Sun can be seen as a system.

A shadow is a 3–D area where light is blocked by an object.

The Moon's phases change from day to day in a cycle that lasts about a month.

Our changing view of sunlight shining on the Moon is what makes the Moon seem to change shape.

A solar eclipse occurs when the Moon blocks sunlight from reaching the Earth.

A lunar eclipse occurs when the Earth blocks sunlight from reaching the Moon.

Overview

This session gives students a chance to review and discuss their Moon observations and generate a list of patterns that they have discovered. They learn that Moon phases change in a cycle that lasts about a month, and they learn the terms for the different phases.

As they discuss the evidence from their observations, students note a correlation between the Moon's phase and its apparent distance from the Sun. They also notice that the curved, outer edge of the Moon always faces toward the Sun. These observations and the discussion in this session prepare students to understand the model that they will use in Session 4.3 to explain the lunar cycle.

The concepts of models and evidence are introduced, and are added to the class concept wall.

Finding the Patterns in Moon Observations	Estimated Time
Summarizing class data from Moon observations	30 minutes
Adding models and evidence concepts to concept wall	15 minutes
TOTAL	**45 minutes**

What You Need

For the class
- ❑ sentence strips for 10 key concepts
- ❑ 1 sheet of chart paper or butcher paper
- ❑ wide-tip felt pen
- ❑ chalkboard or overhead projector

For each student
- ❑ student Moon observations from Session 4.1
- ❑ paper and pencils
- ❑ *optional:* a calculator

TEACHER CONSIDERATIONS

TEACHING NOTES

Wait for Session 4.3 to explain Moon phases: During the discussions in this session, some students may offer explanations for Moon phases or ask you to explain them. Accept their ideas for now, but refrain from providing the explanation until Session 4.3, in which students will experience firsthand a powerful model to explain the phases that they have observed.

Key Vocabulary

Science and Inquiry Vocabulary

Evidence

Scientific Explanation

Model

System

Prediction

Scientist

Scale Model

Three–Dimensional (3–D)

Two–Dimensional (2–D)

Space Science Vocabulary

Crescent Moon

Cycle

Diameter

Solar Eclipse (eclipse of the Sun)

Lunar Eclipse (eclipse of the Moon)

Full Moon

Gibbous

New Moon

Orbit

Phase

Quarter Moon

Satellite

Shadow

Sphere

Rotate

Revolve

Unit Goals

The Earth and Moon move with regular and predictable motion.

The relationship between the Earth, Moon, and Sun can be seen as a system.

A shadow is a 3–D area where light is blocked by an object.

The Moon's phases change from day to day in a cycle that lasts about a month.

Our changing view of sunlight shining on the Moon is what makes the Moon seem to change shape.

A solar eclipse occurs when the Moon blocks sunlight from reaching the Earth.

A lunar eclipse occurs when the Earth blocks sunlight from reaching the Moon.

Getting Ready

1. Write the 10 key concepts that follow on sentence strips and have them ready to post. The first four key concepts will go in the right column of the concept wall under *What We Have Learned About Space Science:*

The Moon can be seen sometimes at night and sometimes during the day.
The shape of the Moon as we see it changes from day to day in a cycle that lasts about a month.
The changes in the way the Moon looks are called phases.
Some of the Moon's phases are: new, crescent, quarter, gibbous, and full.

The other six concepts will go on the *What We Have Learned About Evidence and Models* side of the concept wall:

Scientists use models to understand and explain how things work.
Every model is inaccurate in some way.
A model can be an explanation in your mind.
Evidence is information, such as measurements or observations, that is used to help explain things.
Scientists base their explanations on evidence.
Scientists question, discuss, and check each other's evidence and explanations.

TEACHER CONSIDERATIONS

TEACHING NOTES

Key concepts about models and evidence presented earlier in the Sequence: A total of nine key concepts about models and evidence were presented in Units 1 and 2 of the Sequence. If you presented either or both of those units, leave all those concepts on your concept wall. Because Unit 4 is a shorter unit, we present only six of the key concepts about models. (The same was true for Unit 3.) Just for your information, the additional three concepts about models presented during Units 1 and 2 were:

Space scientists use models to study things that are very big or far away.
Models help us make and test predictions.
Models can be 3–dimensional or 2–dimensional.

Key Vocabulary

Science and Inquiry Vocabulary

Evidence

Scientific Explanation

Model

System

Prediction

Scientist

Scale Model

Three–Dimensional (3–D)

Two–Dimensional (2–D)

Space Science Vocabulary

Crescent Moon

Cycle

Diameter

Solar Eclipse (eclipse of the Sun)

Lunar Eclipse (eclipse of the Moon)

Full Moon

Gibbous

New Moon

Orbit

Phase

Quarter Moon

Satellite

Shadow

Sphere

Rotate

Revolve

Summarizing the Class Data from Moon Observations

This discussion is written for classes who made their observations during the daytime. If your class used the Moon Observations Simulation on the CD-ROM or did their Moon observations in the evening, please see page 437 for how to adjust the discussion.

1. **Review Moon observations.** Tell the class that they will now review and discuss their observations and measurements of the Moon.

2. **Record the average number of fists.** Place a large sheet of chart paper on the wall. Ask students to take out their folders of observations of the Moon. For the first day's observations, poll the class to find out the number of fists between the Sun and the Moon on that day. List their answers on the chalkboard or overhead projector, and then ask them to estimate the average number of fists for that day. You may also have them work out the exact average, using paper and pencil or calculators.

3. **Draw Moon and Sun on chart with dates and average numbers of fists.** Use a marker to draw the Sun and Moon as they appeared on that date. Write the date and the average number of fists next to the Moon. For each day's observation, add one more image of the Moon, the date, and the number of fists. (See illustration on page 435.)

4. **Students describe patterns observed.** Ask students to describe the patterns revealed on the large sheet of paper. Ask questions to help them summarize the patterns as you go from full moon to new moon:

   • Each day, the Moon appears closer to the Sun in the sky.

   • As the Moon moves closer to the Sun, its shape appears thinner.

   • The curved side of the Moon is always on the side facing the Sun.

5. **Introduce Moon phase terms.** Introduce the term *phases* for the different Moon shapes they have observed. Introduce the terms for the different phases. The phase just after the *full moon* is called *gibbous* (*gib*-us). When the Moon appears as a half disk it is technically called a *quarter moon,* but most students prefer to call it a *half moon.* When it is less than a half disk it is called a *crescent,* and when it disappears from view altogether, it is called a *new moon.*

Unit Goals

The Earth and Moon move with regular and predictable motion.

The relationship between the Earth, Moon, and Sun can be seen as a system.

A shadow is a 3–D area where light is blocked by an object.

The Moon's phases change from day to day in a cycle that lasts about a month.

Our changing view of sunlight shining on the Moon is what makes the Moon seem to change shape.

A solar eclipse occurs when the Moon blocks sunlight from reaching the Earth.

A lunar eclipse occurs when the Earth blocks sunlight from reaching the Moon.

TEACHER CONSIDERATIONS

TEACHING NOTES

Introduce the terms waxing and waning: You may want to tell students that as the Moon seems to shrink in size, we say that it is *waning*. During the other half of the lunar cycle, when the Moon appears to grow "fatter," we say that it is *waxing*.

Unit Goals

The Earth and Moon move with regular and predictable motion.

The relationship between the Earth, Moon, and Sun can be seen as a system.

A shadow is a 3–D area where light is blocked by an object.

The Moon's phases change from day to day in a cycle that lasts about a month.

Our changing view of sunlight shining on the Moon is what makes the Moon seem to change shape.

A solar eclipse occurs when the Moon blocks sunlight from reaching the Earth.

A lunar eclipse occurs when the Earth blocks sunlight from reaching the Moon.

6. Define the lunar cycle. Tell the class that the phases of the Moon change in a regular cycle over a period of about a month. Say that the word *cycle* describes any series of events that happen in the same order again and again. Each month, the Moon phases change gradually from new to full, and then back again from full to new. Tell them that this is called the *lunar cycle.*

You might want to tell students that the word month *comes from the word* moon. *And the word* lunar *comes from* luna, *which is the name of Earth's Moon. (It is also the word for* moon *in Spanish.)*

7. Students label phases. Have students write the words *gibbous, quarter moon,* etc. to label the drawings on their observation sheets.

8. Post key concepts about Moon observations. Post the four concepts about Moon observations on the concept wall. Review the concepts with the students, and tell them that they will be finding out more about why the Moon seems to change its shape in the coming sessions.

The Moon can be seen sometimes at night and sometimes during the day.
The shape of the Moon as we see it changes from day to day in a cycle that lasts about a month.
The changes in the way the Moon looks are called phases.
Some of the Moon's phases are: new, crescent, quarter, gibbous, and full.

Adding Key Concepts About Models and Evidence

1. Introduce evidence. Say that all the measurements and observations they have made are *evidence* about the Moon's phases. Tell them that scientists use evidence to help them explain things.

2. Introduce models. Say that people have been wondering for a long time about why the Moon seems to change its shape each month. People have come up with many different explanations, or *models,* for Moon phases.

TEACHER CONSIDERATIONS

SUMMARIZING THE CLASS DATA FROM EVENING OBSERVATIONS OR THE CD–ROM SIMULATION

The CD–ROM simulation uses evening observations. Whether your students used the CD–ROM simulation or did their observations as homework in the evenings, you can use the same procedure for recording as with daytime observations, but with the following adjustments:

1. When you discuss and summarize the evening observations of either the simulation or the real evening sky, your students should notice these patterns as you go from new moon to full moon:

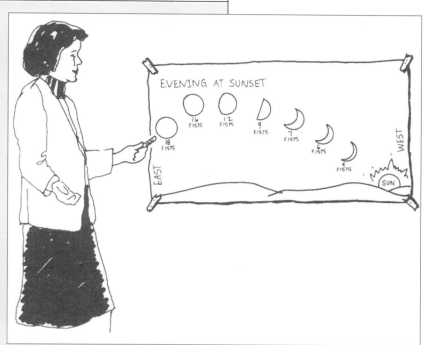

- Each evening, the Moon appears *farther from* the Sun in the sky.

- As the Moon moves *farther from* the Sun, its shape appears *fatter*.

- The curved side of the Moon is always on the side facing the Sun.

2. For the CD-ROM simulation, ask for students' measurements in finger-widths. Record the class average and the date. For the date, you might check the newspaper or a calendar, and use the first four dates after the new Moon as the dates on your chart.

3. On the CD-ROM simulation, the Moon is seen on only four successive nights, so it does not go through all its phases. Students will see a trend from a thin crescent toward the quarter Moon. Tell students that they would see this trend continue in the sky on subsequent evenings, and draw the quarter, gibbous, and full phases for them as you introduce those terms.

TEACHING NOTES

For the CD-ROM simulation: Gather students' measurements of the distance between the Sun and Moon in number of finger-widths instead of fists for each evening.

3. Session 4.3: the scientific model. Tell students that in the next class session, they will get to use a light bulb and spheres to learn about the currently accepted scientific model that explains Moon phases. The model is based on and takes into account all the scientific evidence.

4. Post key concepts. Post the following key concepts on the concept wall. Read them with students, and clarify any terms that they may not have encountered earlier. Emphasize that a model can be a physical object, but it can also simply be a person's explanation for something they have observed.

Scientists use models to understand and explain how things work.
Every model is inaccurate in some way.
A model can be an explanation in your mind.
Evidence is information, such as measurements or observations, that is used to help explain things.
Scientists base their explanations on evidence.
Scientists question, discuss, and check each other's evidence and explanations.

Unit Goals

The Earth and Moon move with regular and predictable motion.

The relationship between the Earth, Moon, and Sun can be seen as a system.

A shadow is a 3–D area where light is blocked by an object.

The Moon's phases change from day to day in a cycle that lasts about a month.

Our changing view of sunlight shining on the Moon is what makes the Moon seem to change shape.

A solar eclipse occurs when the Moon blocks sunlight from reaching the Earth.

A lunar eclipse occurs when the Earth blocks sunlight from reaching the Moon.

TEACHER CONSIDERATIONS

TEACHING NOTES

More on Models: If this is the first time that your students have encountered the concept of models, you may want to take some extra time to explain models and how scientists use them, as is done in Unit 3, Session 3.1, and in earlier units of this sequence.

1. Introduce models. Hold up a scale model car (or any model), and say that a model is something that shows or explains what the real thing is like.

2. All models are different from the real thing in at least one way. Emphasize that good models are similar to the real thing, but no model is exactly the same as the real thing. Ask, "What are some ways that the model car is not exactly the same as a real car?" [It's smaller, it has no motor, the doors don't open, the tires are metal, it doesn't have gas in it, it has no lights, it can't move under its own power, and so on.]

3. Scientists often use models. Say that scientists use models to explain things that they have observed, show how they think things in the natural world work, make predictions, or learn more about things that they can't look at directly. In space science, models are used a lot, because the things being studied are so far away and sometimes very large.

4. A model can be someone's explanation. Say that a model can be someone's explanation for how things work. A model is most likely to be accepted by scientists if it is based on all the evidence, and no evidence contradicts it.

OPTIONAL PROMPT FOR WRITING OR DISCUSSION

You may want to have students use the prompt below for science journal writing at the end of this session or as homework. It could also be used for a discussion or during a final student sharing circle.

- Imagine that you are a person who lived 3,000 years ago. How might you explain the Moon getting larger and smaller in the sky every month?

Key Vocabulary

Science and Inquiry Vocabulary

Evidence

Scientific Explanation

Model

System

Prediction

Scientist

Scale Model

Three–Dimensional (3–D)

Two–Dimensional (2–D)

Space Science Vocabulary

Crescent Moon

Cycle

Diameter

Solar Eclipse (eclipse of the Sun)

Lunar Eclipse (eclipse of the Moon)

Full Moon

Gibbous

New Moon

Orbit

Phase

Quarter Moon

Satellite

Shadow

Sphere

Rotate

Revolve

Unit Goals

The Earth and Moon move with regular and predictable motion.

The relationship between the Earth, Moon, and Sun can be seen as a system.

A shadow is a 3–D area where light is blocked by an object.

The Moon's phases change from day to day in a cycle that lasts about a month.

Our changing view of sunlight shining on the Moon is what makes the Moon seem to change shape.

A solar eclipse occurs when the Moon blocks sunlight from reaching the Earth.

A lunar eclipse occurs when the Earth blocks sunlight from reaching the Moon.

Overview

This session begins with a review of the student observations of the Moon. Why does the Moon appear to change shape, when it is actually always spherical?

To answer the question, students use a model to explain the Moon's monthly cycle of phases. In the model, students form a circle, standing around a light bulb "Sun." Each student's head represents the Earth. Students hold "moon balls" in their outstretched hands and slowly turn to move them in circles around their heads. Because their heads represent the Earth in the model, students are able to observe Moon phases from an Earth perspective. This makes it easier during the following discussions to relate the model to their earlier observations of the Moon and Sun. Five key concepts about the Moon are added to the class concept wall.

In an evidence circle activity, students are challenged to debate which of two explanations on the *Moon Phases Explanations* sheet is best. In groups of four, they attempt to agree on the best explanation, using evidence from the moon ball model, from the *Shadow Play* activity in Session 4.1, and from their Moon observations. After the evidence circle discussion, students individually fill out the *Moon Phases Explanations* sheet, which serves as an embedded assessment of their understanding of Moon phases.

Understanding Moon Phases	Estimated Time
Reviewing Moon observations	5 minutes
Modeling Moon phases	20 minutes
Discussing the Moon phase model and posting key concepts	15 minutes
Evidence circle activity	20 minutes
TOTAL	**60 minutes**

What You Need

For the class
- ❑ lamp, light bulb, extension cord, and tape for taping down cords (from Session 4.1)
- ❑ sentence strips for 5 key concepts
- ❑ wide-tip felt pen
- ❑ chalkboard or overhead projector

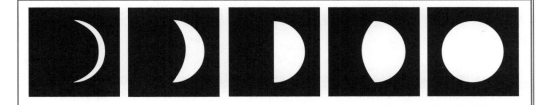

Key Vocabulary

Science and Inquiry Vocabulary

Evidence

Scientific Explanation

Model

System

Prediction

Scientist

Scale Model

Three–Dimensional (3–D)

Two–Dimensional (2–D)

Space Science Vocabulary

Crescent Moon

Cycle

Diameter

Solar Eclipse (eclipse of the Sun)

Lunar Eclipse (eclipse of the Moon)

Full Moon

Gibbous

New Moon

Orbit

Phase

Quarter Moon

Satellite

Shadow

Sphere

Rotate

Revolve

For each student
❑ 1 two-inch polystyrene sphere
❑ 1 pencil
❑ *Moon Phases Explanations* sheet, from the student sheet packet

Getting Ready

1. **Decide if it is necessary to shift student desks for the moon ball activity.** The class will need to stand in a circle around the light bulb with a distance of about an arm's length between each student. You can leave the desks where they are and have students form a circle around some of them. Alternatively, you can have students move desks to the side for the moon ball activity. If you have a large class, you may want to consider conducting this activity with only half the class at a time, while the other half remains seated.

2. **Place the lamp and light bulb in the center of the area where students will stand.** The light bulb should be placed at roughly eye level for most students. Tape the cord down to the floor for safety.

3. **Darken the room.** If you can't darken your classroom completely, find a room for the moon ball activity that you can darken by drawing curtains or by taping black paper over the windows.

4. **Determine which light bulb is best.** Test a moon ball at about the same distance from the lamp as the students will. Observe the contrast between dark and light sides of the sphere, and the shadow it makes on the desk. If necessary, change the bulb, and again observe the contrast. Practice modeling moon phases, as described under *Modeling Moon Phases* beginning on page 444.

5. **Make one copy for each student of the *Moon Phases Explanations* sheet.**

6. **Have the moon balls ready to distribute.** You can put pencils in them ahead of time to serve as holders, or have students insert their own pencils during the activity.

Unit Goals

The Earth and Moon move with regular and predictable motion.

The relationship between the Earth, Moon, and Sun can be seen as a system.

A shadow is a 3–D area where light is blocked by an object.

The Moon's phases change from day to day in a cycle that lasts about a month.

Our changing view of sunlight shining on the Moon is what makes the Moon seem to change shape.

A solar eclipse occurs when the Moon blocks sunlight from reaching the Earth.

A lunar eclipse occurs when the Earth blocks sunlight from reaching the Moon.

TEACHER CONSIDERATIONS

TEACHING NOTES

Adjust for low ceilings or white walls: Try to set up your light bulb as far as possible from white walls, which can reflect light. In some classrooms, a low, white ceiling can reflect light on the moon balls, making it harder to see the Moon phases created by light from the bulb. If this is the case, a lower-watt bulb may be best. If necessary, try holding a piece of cardboard or other flat object above the bulb during the activity.

Practice with the moon balls: Even if you are confident in your understanding of what causes Moon phases, as well as solar eclipses and lunar eclipses, be sure to make time to familiarize yourself with the model and how it works before presenting the activity to your students. This will make the lessons more smooth and effective (and fun). Familiarizing yourself with the model is even more important if you, like many adults, are at all unsure about what causes the phases.

What One Teacher Said

"Understanding Moon phases is a difficult concept. I thought the 'Modeling Moon Phases' activity was excellent! It really helped ME visualize what's going on during Moon phases!"

7. Prepare sentence strips for the following five key space science concepts. Have them ready to post after the moon ball activity on the *What We Have Learned About Space Science* side of the concept wall:

The Moon seems to change shape from day to day, but it is always round like a sphere.
It takes the Moon about a month to orbit the Earth once.
Phases of the Moon are not caused by Earth's shadow.
Our changing view of sunlight shining on the Moon is what makes the Moon seem to change shape.
The Sun, Earth, and Moon form a system.

A Brief Review Before the Activity

1. Review the lunar cycle. Ask, "What are the different shapes, or phases, of the Moon called?" [Full, gibbous, quarter, crescent, and new.] How long does it take for the Moon to go through one cycle of phases? [About a month.]

2. Ask, "What shape is the Moon?" [Round like a sphere.]

3. Why does the Moon seem to change its shape? Ask, "Does the Moon really change its shape?" [No, it's always spherical.] Ask, "If the Moon is always round like a sphere, why does it look as though it has different shapes at different times?" [Encourage several answers.]

Modeling Moon Phases

1. Arrange your students so that they are standing in a circle around the lamp. Explain that in this model, the light bulb will represent the Sun and their heads will represent the Earth. They will each have a sphere, or "moon ball," to represent the Moon.

TEACHER CONSIDERATIONS

TEACHING NOTES

Eclipses in Session 4.4: During the Moon phase model in this session, some students may discover solar eclipses as their model moons block the Sun, or lunar eclipses as their moons enter the shadow of their heads. We have purposely delayed the modeling eclipses activity until Session 4.4 to avoid confusion, but if any students discover eclipses, acknowledge it now, and tell them that in the next session they'll be learning more about eclipses.

QUICK CHECK FOR UNDERSTANDING

Spherical shape of the Moon: If students say that the Moon is round, ask if they mean round like a plate or round like a sphere.

PROVIDING MORE EXPERIENCE

If students indicate that they think the Moon is round like a plate, take some time to present the activities in the first two class sessions of Unit 2, in which students gather evidence about the spherical shape of the Earth, and extend that understanding to the Moon and stars.

QUICK CHECK FOR UNDERSTANDING

Incorrect explanations for Moon phases: It is helpful to note students' ideas about why the Moon changes shape now, so that you can help students address misconceptions later in the session during the moon ball model. When asked why the Moon has different shapes at different times, some commonly expressed ideas are, "The Earth's shadow is on the Moon" or "Clouds are blocking the Moon." These ideas seem reasonable because the Moon does pass into the shadow of the Earth occasionally, and clouds do cover the Moon sometimes. However, they are not correct explanations for the phases of the Moon.

What Some Teachers Said

"*They really liked working with their 'Earth model' and with the moon model. About half of the students were not able to see the phase shadows in the beginning. But with help everyone was able to spot the shadow's shape. It's too bad there wasn't a tape recorder playing so you could hear their oohs and aahs once they discovered the shadow and saw the lighted part change shape as the Moon went around the Earth.*"

"*Kids really enjoyed it and it helped them to understand that the Moon's shape does not change and it helped them to understand the phases better.*"

"*It was great to see the students truly understood that the Moon does not change size. I was shocked to realize that they actually thought it did!*"

"*The moon ball experiment was a hit! All of my students were able to identify the phases as we progressed through the cycle and the concept of the Sun, Earth, and Moon as a system was very easy to grasp.*"

Unit Goals

The Earth and Moon move with regular and predictable motion.

The relationship between the Earth, Moon, and Sun can be seen as a system.

A shadow is a 3–D area where light is blocked by an object.

The Moon's phases change from day to day in a cycle that lasts about a month.

Our changing view of sunlight shining on the Moon is what makes the Moon seem to change shape.

A solar eclipse occurs when the Moon blocks sunlight from reaching the Earth.

A lunar eclipse occurs when the Earth blocks sunlight from reaching the Moon.

2. **Turn on lamp and darken room.** Turn on the light bulb in the center of the circle of students. Darken the room so that the only light comes from the light bulb.

3. **Distribute moon balls.** Before passing out the moon balls, caution students not to play inappropriately with them. Hand out moon balls and pencil "handles."

4. **Face the "Sun" and hold up the moon ball.** Ask your students to hold their moon balls out in front of them in either hand, directly in front of the "Sun." Mention that if their arm gets tired during the activity, they should quietly switch to the other arm.

5. **Thin crescent.** Tell students that the Moon orbits the Earth. Instruct students to move the moon ball to the left until they can see a thin, bright crescent lit up on the ball, and then stop (crescent moon).

6. **Check for student understanding.** Check to make sure that everyone can see the crescent-shaped light on the moon ball. The most common error that students make is not moving the moon ball far enough to the left. Another error is looking at the light bulb and ignoring the "Moon." Help individuals as needed.

7. **Does the curved, bright side of the moon ball face toward or away from the Sun?** When everyone can see the crescent of light, ask, "Is the curved, bright edge of your moon facing toward the Sun, or away from it?" [Toward the Sun, as in observations of the real Moon.]

8. **Continue the orbit to the quarter Moon.** Tell students to continue orbiting their moons around their heads in the same direction, until exactly half of the "Moon" is lit (quarter moon). (They will, of course, need to turn their bodies to the left, too.) Ask, "As the Moon appears fuller, does it move toward the Sun or away from it?" [Away from the Sun, just like the real Moon.] Again, ask if the curved part of the Moon faces toward or away from the Sun. [Toward.]

9. **Gibbous Moon.** Tell students to continue turning and orbiting their moon ball in the same direction, until it is halfway between a quarter Moon and a full Moon (gibbous).

10. **Full Moon.** Have them continue moving the moon ball in its orbit until the part that they see is fully lit (full moon). Their backs should now be to the light bulb. Explain that they will have to hold the moon ball just above the shadow of their heads. Ask, "When the Moon is full, is it between you and the Sun, or on the opposite side of you from the Sun?" [It is on the opposite side of you from the Sun.]

TEACHER CONSIDERATIONS

TEACHING NOTES

Classroom management with the moon ball activity: This activity is exciting and extremely effective, but it can pose management problems, especially in large classes. Caution the class ahead of time that students who behave inappropriately will have to leave the circle and sit down. Common management problems include playing with moon balls inappropriately, going up to the light bulb and putting the moon ball right near the light, and holding side conversations that make it hard for everyone to follow the activity.

Define Orbit: In previous units of the Sequence, especially Unit 2, the concept of *orbit* was explored. If this is your students' first exposure to the concept, introduce orbits by asking the following questions:

- What is meant by the term *orbit?* [To travel around something in space.]

- Can you name something that orbits around something else? [Earth and the other eight planets orbit around the Sun.]

- Can you name anything that orbits around the Earth? [Space shuttles, the International Space Station, the Moon, satellites, and so on.]

- What is a satellite? [Any object that orbits another object. The Moon is a natural satellite of Earth, and the International Space Station is a human-made satellite, sometimes called an artificial satellite.]

Key Vocabulary

Science and Inquiry Vocabulary

Evidence

Scientific Explanation

Model

System

Prediction

Scientist

Scale Model

Three–Dimensional (3–D)

Two–Dimensional (2–D)

Space Science Vocabulary

Crescent Moon

Cycle

Diameter

Solar Eclipse (eclipse of the Sun)

Lunar Eclipse (eclipse of the Moon)

Full Moon

Gibbous

New Moon

Orbit

Phase

Quarter Moon

Satellite

Shadow

Sphere

Rotate

Revolve

Unit Goals

The Earth and Moon move with regular and predictable motion.

The relationship between the Earth, Moon, and Sun can be seen as a system.

A shadow is a 3–D area where light is blocked by an object.

The Moon's phases change from day to day in a cycle that lasts about a month.

Our changing view of sunlight shining on the Moon is what makes the Moon seem to change shape.

A solar eclipse occurs when the Moon blocks sunlight from reaching the Earth.

A lunar eclipse occurs when the Earth blocks sunlight from reaching the Moon.

11. Gibbous Moon Again. Tell students to continue moving the "Moon" in its orbit until it is gibbous once again.

12. Move another quarter turn. Instruct students to continue orbiting the moon ball in the same direction until it is just half full again (quarter moon). Ask, "As the Moon moves toward the Sun, does it appear to get fuller or thinner?" [Thinner.] "Is the curved side facing toward or away from the Sun?" [Toward.]

13. Model thin crescent and then new moon. Finally, tell students to continue to move their moon balls so that they see very thin crescents again. Explain that most of the time the Moon does not pass directly in front of the Sun, but just above or below the Sun. When the Moon cannot be seen at all, this phase is called the new moon. (It is called new because it is at the beginning of its cycle. Some ancient peoples thought that a brand new moon was being born at this time!) Tell them that they have modeled one full cycle of the Moon, which takes a month.

14. Do another orbit, focusing on light and shadows. Direct students through another orbit. This time, instruct them to pause at various points, and ask them questions about light and shadow.
  • What is making the bright side of the Moon bright? [Light from the Sun.]
  • What is making the dark side of the Moon dark? [The beginning of the Moon's own shadow.]
  Note: This is a particularly important question, because many students think that the dark part is caused by the shadow of the Earth.
  • Using a finger from your other hand, can you find places around your Moon that are also in shadow?

15. Do a few orbits. Have students turn and move their moon balls in orbits several times until they seem to fully grasp why the Moon goes through phases.

Discussing the Moon Phase Model

1. Lights on, students seated, and moon balls collected. Turn on the room lights, and have students be seated. Collect the moon balls.

2. Relate the model to observations of the real Moon. Help students relate the model to their observations of the real Moon. If they watched the Moon in the evenings, they saw it go from crescent to full and move farther from the Sun. Remind students that when they watched the Moon in the daytime, it got thinner as it got closer to the Sun.

TEACHER CONSIDERATIONS

SCIENCE NOTES

There is no need to bring the following issues up with students unless they ask, but in case they should arise:

Why turn to the left? Turning left correctly models the direction of Earth's spin. If you imagine looking down from the ceiling at the model, the North Pole would be at the top of the student's head. As the students turn to the left, they model the direction that the real Earth rotates: counterclockwise, when seen from above.

The "dark side" of the Moon: This expression is sometimes used incorrectly to describe the side of the Moon that is always facing away from the Earth, due to the gravitational lock that the Earth has with the Moon. As can be seen through the model in this session, the far side of the Moon is *not* always dark. During the new moon, for example, the far side of the Moon is in full Sun. There is always a side of the Moon that is dark at any given moment, but it is always changing. For more information, see *Background for Teachers* on page 41.

Key Vocabulary

Science and Inquiry Vocabulary

Evidence

Scientific Explanation

Model

System

Prediction

Scientist

Scale Model

Three–Dimensional (3–D)

Two–Dimensional (2–D)

Space Science Vocabulary

Crescent Moon

Cycle

Diameter

Solar Eclipse (eclipse of the Sun)

Lunar Eclipse (eclipse of the Moon)

Full Moon

Gibbous

New Moon

Orbit

Phase

Quarter Moon

Satellite

Shadow

Sphere

Rotate

Revolve

Unit Goals

The Earth and Moon move with regular and predictable motion.

The relationship between the Earth, Moon, and Sun can be seen as a system.

A shadow is a 3–D area where light is blocked by an object.

The Moon's phases change from day to day in a cycle that lasts about a month.

Our changing view of sunlight shining on the Moon is what makes the Moon seem to change shape.

A solar eclipse occurs when the Moon blocks sunlight from reaching the Earth.

A lunar eclipse occurs when the Earth blocks sunlight from reaching the Moon.

3. **Ask again why the Moon seems to change its shape.** Students may now be able to answer the question, "If the Moon is really a sphere, why does it sometimes look like a crescent or half moon?" The explanation for Moon phases may be hard to put into words, but students should mention:

- Moon phases have to do with the Sun's light on the Moon.

- We see only the part of the Moon that is lit by the Sun. The rest of the Moon is there, but it is dark and we can't see it.

- As the Moon moves, we see the Sun's light on it from different directions, and we see more or less of the lighted part.

- The dark parts of the Moon are caused by the beginning of the Moon's own shadow.

4. **The Moon doesn't shine with its own light.** Ask, "In our model, where did the light on the Moon come from?" [The light bulb "Sun."] Emphasize that the Moon doesn't shine with its own light.

5. **Review concept of "beginning of a shadow."** Remind students of the key concept posted during the *Shadow Play* activity in Session 4.1: *"The shadow begins on the dark side of the object that is blocking the light."*

6. **One Moon orbit is one month.** Tell students that a full orbit of the Moon around the Earth takes about a month (more precisely, 29.53 days). Tell them that the Moon cycle has been used by people since ancient times to mark time.

7. **Review that one Earth spin is one day.** Ask how long it takes for the Earth to spin. [One day.] Point out that in the model they just did, students didn't model the Earth's daily spin. In reality, the Earth spins about 29 times each time the Moon orbits the Earth one time.

8. **One Earth orbit around the Sun is one year.** Ask how long it takes for the Earth to orbit the Sun once. [365 days.]

9. **The Earth, Moon, and Sun are a system.** Say that scientists think of the Earth, Moon, and Sun as a *system*: a group of objects that interact.

TEACHER CONSIDERATIONS

TEACHING NOTES

Common Misconceptions about Reflected Light: The concepts involved in reflected light are not the primary focus of this unit. However, during student discussion about Moon phases, it is helpful to be aware of common student ideas about reflected light. Research shows that students understand that mirrors reflect light, but may have difficulty understanding that other objects do, too. Even more difficult for some students to accept is the idea that our eyes are "light detectors," and that we do not perceive an object unless light from the object enters our eyes. The reason we do not see the dark part of the Moon is that no light from that part of the Moon is reaching our eyes. A good resource for helping students understand reflection and the nature of light and color is the GEMS unit *Color Analyzers.*

SCIENCE NOTES

"Earthshine" on the Moon: Don't bring this up with students unless it's appropriate, but sometimes, when we look at a crescent moon in the evening, we can see the rest of the Moon, too, only much more faintly. The bright crescent is, of course, reflected sunlight. What is the light on the other part of the Moon? It is sunlight reflected from the Earth onto the Moon ("Earthshine")!

Unit Goals

The Earth and Moon move with regular and predictable motion.

The relationship between the Earth, Moon, and Sun can be seen as a system.

A shadow is a 3–D area where light is blocked by an object.

The Moon's phases change from day to day in a cycle that lasts about a month.

Our changing view of sunlight shining on the Moon is what makes the Moon seem to change shape.

A solar eclipse occurs when the Moon blocks sunlight from reaching the Earth.

A lunar eclipse occurs when the Earth blocks sunlight from reaching the Moon.

10. **Post the key concepts.** On the concept wall, post the five key concepts that follow. Read them with students.

The Moon seems to change shape from day to day, but it is always round like a sphere.
It takes the Moon about a month to orbit the Earth once.
Phases of the Moon are not caused by Earth's shadow.
Our changing view of sunlight shining on the Moon is what makes the Moon seem to change shape.
The Sun, Earth, and Moon form a system.

Evidence Circles: Moon Phase Explanations

1. **Reflect on how the model explains Moon phases.** Tell the class that you would like them to have more time to think about, discuss, and write about what they have learned about Moon phases.

2. **Evidence circles.** Arrange students in groups of four. Hold up a student sheet, and say that there are two explanations on the sheet for Moon phases. Only one of the explanations fits the evidence they saw in their Moon observations and in the moon ball model.

3. **Procedure.** In their evidence circle, one student will read Explanation #1 aloud. Then, each student will have a turn to say if they agree or disagree with the explanation, and give reasons why. If possible, students should give evidence to back up their thinking.

TEACHER CONSIDERATIONS

TEACHING NOTES

Evidence Circles—Adjusting for Student Experience: The evidence circle format is used frequently in this sequence to help students develop skills involved in evidence-based argumentation. If this is your students' first experience with evidence circles, spend some extra time introducing the procedure, as follows:

1. What is evidence? *Evidence is information, such as measurements or observations, that is used to help explain things.* Say that they gathered evidence during their Moon observations, during the *Shadow Play* activity, and with the moon ball model. Remind them of the key concepts about evidence posted in Session 4.2.

2. Scientists discuss evidence from their investigations. Let students know that one way scientists do their work is to discuss the evidence from their investigations. They listen to one another, ask questions, present evidence, argue, and try to agree about the best explanation—what explanation best matches all available scientific evidence.

3. The Procedure for Evidence Circles. Tell the class that they are going to be discussing something in small groups called evidence circles. As scientists, they will listen to one another, ask questions, raise issues, discuss differing opinions, and try to agree. Explain the procedure:

    a. Each student says what he or she thinks and the reasons why.
    b. The group members discuss among themselves to see if they can come to agreement.

4. Scientists are open to changing their minds based on evidence. The main point of evidence circles is to think about and discuss ideas and evidence in order to find the best explanation for something. Say one of the signs of a true scientist is the ability to listen to others and change your mind when you find that what you think doesn't match the evidence.

Optional—**Allow students to use moon balls during evidence circles:** During the evidence circle activity, you might want to give each team of students a moon ball to use to confirm or refute each explanation. This would mean arranging the desks around the light bulb, as in Session 4.1, and darkening the room.

What One Teacher Said

"Fabulous. This made all concepts so clear. When you read their post comments, you can see that many used the moon ball activity for evidence."

4. Model the procedure with the whole class. Write the following sample explanation on the board. (This sample is not one of the explanations on the sheet.)

What causes Moon phases to change during the month?

	Sample Explanation: "Clouds cover part of the Moon."
Do you agree or disagree?	Why? What is the *evidence* for or against this explanation?

a. Ask a student to read the sample explanation aloud.

b. Ask a few students to say if they agree or disagree and why. Help students apply evidence to their arguments. Some possible evidence that students might offer to refute this statement:

- The Moon changes phases even when there are no clouds in the sky.

- Clouds don't have straight edges, so they can't make a straight line shape like the quarter moon.

- I saw the quarter moon in the sky for many hours one day. Clouds wouldn't be steady enough to keep it that shape for hours.

- Clouds couldn't make phases happen because they are not orderly, and phases happen in a certain order every month.

c. After each person in an evidence circle has had a turn to speak, each student decides if he or she agrees or disagrees with the explanation and writes down evidence to back up his or her thinking. Say that students can use evidence from any of the activities they have done so far in the unit:
- the *Shadow Play* activity in Session 4.1
- their Moon observations
- the moon ball model

Unit Goals

The Earth and Moon move with regular and predictable motion.

The relationship between the Earth, Moon, and Sun can be seen as a system.

A shadow is a 3–D area where light is blocked by an object.

The Moon's phases change from day to day in a cycle that lasts about a month.

Our changing view of sunlight shining on the Moon is what makes the Moon seem to change shape.

A solar eclipse occurs when the Moon blocks sunlight from reaching the Earth.

A lunar eclipse occurs when the Earth blocks sunlight from reaching the Moon.

TEACHER CONSIDERATIONS

ASSESSMENT OPPORTUNITY

Critical Juncture—Understanding the Moon's phases may be gradual:
Even after they have seen phase change in the model with their own eyes, student misconceptions about reflected light and the nature of light and shadow can sometimes delay a full understanding of Moon phases. Students may cling to the incorrect idea that it is the Earth's shadow that causes phases. Earth's shadow does, however, cause lunar eclipses. Because of potential confusion, it is preferable for students to have a good understanding of Moon phases before moving on to investigating eclipses in Session 4.4.

QUESTIONNAIRE CONNECTION

Discussion of the first two questions on the *Pre-Unit 4 Questionnaire* can help you get a sense of student understanding.

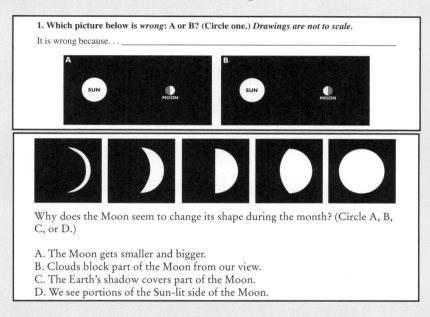

In Question #1, picture A is wrong: You might want to draw the illustrations for Question #1 on the board or overhead for discussion. Ask students to explain why picture A is wrong. Focus their attention on whether the light side of the Moon is facing toward or away from the Sun. [It is incorrect because the bright side of the Moon should be facing the Sun, as in picture B.] Review that it is the Sun's light shining on the Moon that makes part of the Moon bright. Sunlight can't go around the Moon.

Question #2, Why does the Moon seem to change its shape during the month? Read and discuss the four possible answers. Poll students about which answer they think is correct. If you notice that some students still think that clouds (answer B) are the reason, review the evidence that contradicts this. For those who still believe that the Earth's shadow causes phases (answer C), the *Shadows of Mystery Objects* activity and discussion at the beginning of Session 4.4 may help them change their ideas.

Key Vocabulary

Science and Inquiry Vocabulary

Evidence

Scientific Explanation

Model

System

Prediction

Scientist

Scale Model

Three–Dimensional (3–D)

Two–Dimensional (2–D)

Space Science Vocabulary

Crescent Moon

Cycle

Diameter

Solar Eclipse (eclipse of the Sun)

Lunar Eclipse (eclipse of the Moon)

Full Moon

Gibbous

New Moon

Orbit

Phase

Quarter Moon

Satellite

Shadow

Sphere

Rotate

Revolve

MOON PHASE EXPLANATION

Name:_____

Moon Phase Explanations

1	2	3	4	5
thin crescent	fatter crescent	quarter	gibbous	full

What causes Moon phases to change during the month?

Explanation #1
"The Earth's shadow covers part of the Moon."

Do you agree or disagree?	Why? What is the *evidence* for or against this explanation?

Explanation #2
"We see different portions of the Sun-lit side of the Moon."

Do you agree or disagree?	Why? What is the *evidence* for or against this explanation?

5. Give each student a copy of the *Moon Phase Explanations* sheet. Circulate and help students who are having trouble by asking what they saw (evidence), and how that backs up (or refutes) the explanation. For example, ask, "What did you see on the moon ball when you moved it?" [The light part got bigger and smaller.] "Does that make you agree or disagree with Explanation #2?" [Agree, because from Earth we see the light part of the moon ball just as we see sunlight on the real Moon.]

6. Collect their *Moon Phases Explanations* sheets. Tell the class that they will have more opportunities to think about Moon phases, and they will also learn about what causes eclipses in the next session.

TEACHER CONSIDERATIONS

ASSESSMENT OPPORTUNITY

Embedded Assessment—The *Moon Phases Explanations* sheet: A suggested rubric is provided below for scoring. If you notice that many of your students are still confused about the causes of Moon phases, consider doing one or more of the Providing More Experience activities that follow before moving on to Session 4.4. The *Moon Phases Explanations* sheet can be scored using the specific Understanding Science Concepts rubric below or using the general rubrics provided on page 66.

The sheet includes two possible explanations regarding what causes moon phases and the student must decide if they agree or disagree with each explanation and provide evidence for their decision. Please note that it may be difficult for students to put the evidence into words, so a score of 4 requires the student write only one piece of evidence.

Understanding Science Concepts: The key science concepts for this assessment are: 1. Phases of the Moon are *not* caused by Earth's shadow 2. Our changing view of sunlight shining on the Moon is what makes the Moon seem to change shape.	
4	*Complete Understanding:* The student disagrees with Explanation #1 and agrees with Explanation #2. Student uses at least one piece of evidence to refute Explanation #1 and/or support Explanation #2. The evidence can be from the *Shadow Play* activity, the moon ball model, or student Moon observations, or other. Some examples of evidence that can be used to refute Explanation #1, *The Earth's shadow covers part of the Moon:* • The Moon has shadow on it like the sphere in Shadow Play, but the shadow is made by the Moon's shadow on itself, not the Earth's shadow. • From the moon ball model activity, I saw the light on the Moon changing shapes, and it was not because of the Earth's shadow. Some examples of evidence supporting Explanation #2, *We see different portions of the Sun-lit side of the Moon.* • The light and shadow on the ball in Shadow Play looked like Moon phases. This is evidence that phases are caused by light and shadow. • When I moved the moon ball around my head, the light part of the ball looked bigger and smaller. That is like the real Moon with sunlight on it.
3	*Partial Understanding:* The student disagrees with Explanation #1 and agrees with Explanation #2. However, the student does not use evidence from the shadow play activity, their Moon observations, or the moon ball model activities. The support for the explanation they give may be more general or rely on statements of presumed fact, rather than being drawn directly from evidence in classroom science experiences.
2	*Insufficient Understanding.* The student correctly agrees or disagrees with one of the explanations, but not both. The student does not use evidence to support or refute the explanations.
1	*The information is inaccurate.* The student agrees with the incorrect explanation that "the Earth's shadow covers part of the Moon." The student disagrees with the correct explanation that "We see different portions of the Sun-lit side of the Moon." No evidence is provided to support either argument.
0	*The response is irrelevant or off topic.*
n/a	*The student has no opportunity to respond and has left the question blank*

Key Vocabulary

Science and Inquiry Vocabulary

Evidence

Scientific Explanation

Model

System

Prediction

Scientist

Scale Model

Three–Dimensional (3–D)

Two–Dimensional (2–D)

Space Science Vocabulary

Crescent Moon

Cycle

Diameter

Solar Eclipse (eclipse of the Sun)

Lunar Eclipse (eclipse of the Moon)

Full Moon

Gibbous

New Moon

Orbit

Phase

Quarter Moon

Satellite

Shadow

Sphere

Rotate

Revolve

Unit Goals

The Earth and Moon move with regular and predictable motion.

The relationship between the Earth, Moon, and Sun can be seen as a system.

A shadow is a 3–D area where light is blocked by an object.

The Moon's phases change from day to day in a cycle that lasts about a month.

Our changing view of sunlight shining on the Moon is what makes the Moon seem to change shape.

A solar eclipse occurs when the Moon blocks sunlight from reaching the Earth.

A lunar eclipse occurs when the Earth blocks sunlight from reaching the Moon.

TEACHER CONSIDERATIONS

PROVIDING MORE EXPERIENCE

1. Review *Shadow Play* activity. Remind students of their observations on the sphere during the *Shadow Play* activity in Session 4.1. Remind them of the three parts of a shadow, and that the Moon's shadow on itself is making part of the Moon dark. Have them look over their student sheets to see whether the shadow side of the Moon faces toward or away from the Sun.

2. Students present moon ball model to others. Often, teaching a concept to someone else helps learners gain a more solid understanding of that concept. You may want to have your students present the moon ball model to students from another class or to their families at home as homework.

3. Comparing the moon balls model with the real Moon. On a day when you know the real Moon will be visible in the morning, take your students outside with their moon balls. This will work best when the Sun is still low in the sky. Using the Sun's light instead of a light bulb, have them try to find the position of their moon ball that matches the phase of the Moon in the sky.

OPTIONAL PROMPTS FOR WRITING OR DISCUSSION

You may want to have students use the prompts that follow for science journal writing at the end of this session or as homework. They could also be used for a discussion or during a final student sharing circle.

- Do you think that these objects would have phases like the Moon? Why or why not?
  Venus
  Sun

- Draw the light bulb and moon ball model when there was a crescent moon, including shadows.

Key Vocabulary

Science and Inquiry Vocabulary

Evidence

Scientific Explanation

Model

System

Prediction

Scientist

Scale Model

Three–Dimensional (3–D)

Two–Dimensional (2–D)

Space Science Vocabulary

Crescent Moon

Cycle

Diameter

Solar Eclipse (eclipse of the Sun)

Lunar Eclipse (eclipse of the Moon)

Full Moon

Gibbous

New Moon

Orbit

Phase

Quarter Moon

Satellite

Shadow

Sphere

Rotate

Revolve

Unit Goals

The Earth and Moon move with regular and predictable motion.

The relationship between the Earth, Moon, and Sun can be seen as a system.

A shadow is a 3–D area where light is blocked by an object.

The Moon's phases change from day to day in a cycle that lasts about a month.

Our changing view of sunlight shining on the Moon is what makes the Moon seem to change shape.

A solar eclipse occurs when the Moon blocks sunlight from reaching the Earth.

A lunar eclipse occurs when the Earth blocks sunlight from reaching the Moon.

Overview

In the Session 4.3, the students modeled movements in the Earth–Moon–Sun system and learned the real reasons for the phases of the Moon. Still, some students may have lingering doubts about whether the Earth's shadow somehow causes Moon phases. So, before moving on to model lunar and solar eclipses, students gather a bit more evidence to support the scientific model of Moon phases.

They begin by predicting the shape of several mystery objects placed on the overhead projector. The objects are hidden from view, but students are able to see the shadows. They learn that an object's shadow can provide evidence of the shape of an object, although it's difficult to determine whether the object is two- or three-dimensional.

Next, they look at pictures of the Moon in two different phases, crescent and quarter Moon. They see why a person looking at a crescent moon might think that Earth's curved shadow is causing the Moon's shape to look that way. But if a person examines the shape of the quarter phase, he or she will find evidence that contradicts that idea: a round Earth could not make a straight-edged shadow on the Moon.

Having further established that Moon phases are not caused by Earth's shadow, students now focus on celestial events that *are* caused by Earth's shadow: eclipses of the Moon. Returning to the moon ball model, they gather around a light bulb to simulate an eclipse of the Moon. Then, students simulate an eclipse of the Sun.

These concepts are reviewed and applied to the real world as the students are shown photographs of real eclipses of the Moon and Sun. The last two key concepts are added to the concept wall. Finally, students apply their knowledge as they draw an eclipse of the Moon and one of the Sun in *Eclipse Pamphlets*.

Understanding Eclipses of the Moon and Sun	Estimated Time
Shadows of Mystery Objects	15 minutes
Modeling Lunar and Solar eclipses	15 minutes
Photos of eclipse of the Sun and Moon	15 minutes
Making an *Eclipse Pamphlet*	15 minutes
TOTAL	**60 minutes**

TEACHER CONSIDERATIONS

What You Need

For the class

- ❑ lamp, light bulb, extension cord, and tape for taping down cords, as in Session 4.1
- ❑ overhead projector or computer with large screen monitor/LCD projector
- ❑ CD–ROM files or 3 overhead transparencies from the transparency packet: *Crescent and Quarter Moon Phases, Eclipse of the Sun,* and *Eclipse of the Moon*
- ❑ masking tape
- ❑ 2 manila folders
- ❑ 1 opaque film canister
- ❑ 1 die or cube
- ❑ 1 two–dimensional square, cut out of paper or cardboard
- ❑ 1 coin
- ❑ 1 small ball (or marble), about the same diameter as the coin
- ❑ sentence strips for 2 key concepts
- ❑ wide–tip felt pen

For each student

- ❑ 1 two-inch polystyrene ball from Session 4.1
- ❑ 1 pencil
- ❑ *Eclipse Pamphlet* student sheet, from the student sheet packet

Getting Ready

Getting Ready for Observing Shadows of Mystery Objects

1. Tape two manila folders to the overhead projector as a screen to prevent students from seeing the mystery objects you will place on the overhead projector.

2. Cut out a square piece of paper about the same size as the cube. Set the five objects (paper square, cube, coin, small ball, and film canister) inside the area, shielded from view by the manila folders, but not on the glass of the projector.

3. Put a very small piece of tape on the underside of the ball to keep it from rolling when you set it on the overhead projector.

4. Photocopy an *Eclipse Pamphlet* sheet for each student.

Unit Goals

The Earth and Moon move with regular and predictable motion.

The relationship between the Earth, Moon, and Sun can be seen as a system.

A shadow is a 3–D area where light is blocked by an object.

The Moon's phases change from day to day in a cycle that lasts about a month.

Our changing view of sunlight shining on the Moon is what makes the Moon seem to change shape.

A solar eclipse occurs when the Moon blocks sunlight from reaching the Earth.

A lunar eclipse occurs when the Earth blocks sunlight from reaching the Moon.

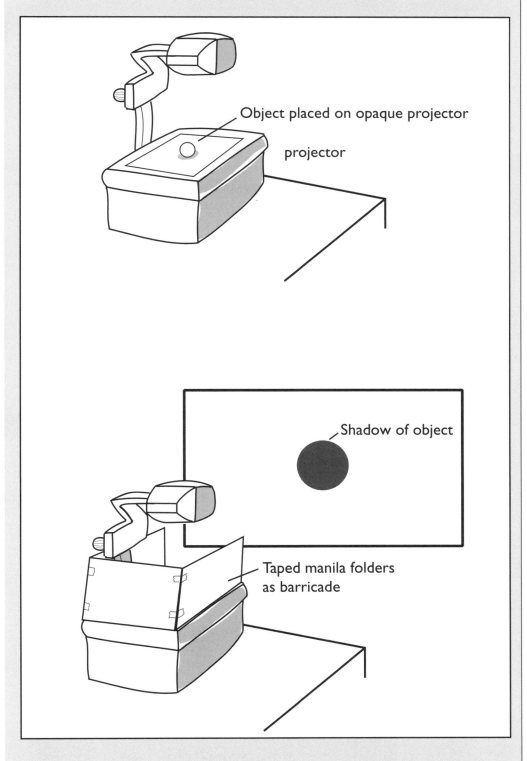

Object placed on opaque projector

projector

Shadow of object

Taped manila folders
as barricade

Key Vocabulary

**Science and
Inquiry Vocabulary**

Evidence

Scientific Explanation

Model

System

Prediction

Scientist

Scale Model

Three–Dimensional (3–D)

Two–Dimensional (2–D)

Space Science Vocabulary

Crescent Moon

Cycle

Diameter

Solar Eclipse (eclipse
of the Sun)

Lunar Eclipse (eclipse
of the Moon)

Full Moon

Gibbous

New Moon

Orbit

Phase

Quarter Moon

Satellite

Shadow

Sphere

Rotate

Revolve

5. Make a sample *Eclipse Pamphlet* by folding one of the *Eclipse Pamphlet* sheets along the two dotted lines. Label the outside of the pamphlet with the words *Eclipses*, *Solar*, and *Lunar*. (See illustrations on page 465). Don't draw in the Moon or shadows on your sample.

6. If you will not be using the CD–ROM, make overhead transparencies

7. Arrange for the appropriate projector format (computer with large screen monitor, LCD projector, or overhead projector) to display images to the class.

8. Set up the light bulb and extension cord as in the Session 4.1 so that students can stand in a circle around it to model eclipses.

9. Have moon balls ready to give to your students.

10. Write the 2 key concepts that follow on sentence strips and have them ready to post on the concept wall under *What We Have Learned About Space Science*.

> We see an eclipse of the Sun when the Moon goes in front of the Sun. This is called a solar eclipse.

> We see an eclipse of the Moon when the Moon goes into the Earth's shadow. This is called a lunar eclipse.

Observing Shadows of Mystery Objects

Note: Keep the film canister, cube, paper square, marble, and coin out of sight near the overhead projector before this activity. Place two manila folders or books on the overhead projector so that students won't be able to see the objects when you put them on the projector.

1. **Evidence from moon balls model.** Ask the class to think about the moon ball activity in the previous session. Remind them that this is the model that scientists agree best explains Moon phases. Ask if seeing the evidence of changing light on the moon in the model changed any of your students' ideas about what causes Moon phases.

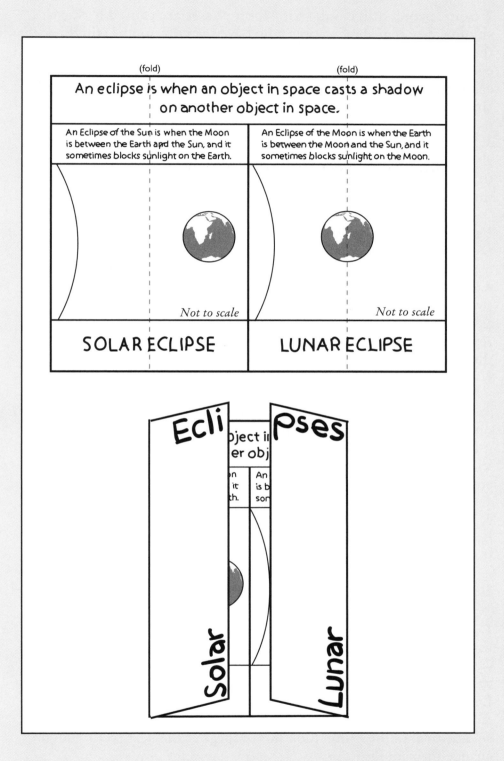

(fold)   (fold)

An eclipse is when an object in space casts a shadow on another object in space.

An Eclipse of the Sun is when the Moon is between the Earth and the Sun, and it sometimes blocks sunlight on the Earth.	An Eclipse of the Moon is when the Earth is between the Moon and the Sun, and it sometimes blocks sunlight on the Moon.
Not to scale	*Not to scale*
SOLAR ECLIPSE	**LUNAR ECLIPSE**

Unit Goals

The Earth and Moon move with regular and predictable motion.

The relationship between the Earth, Moon, and Sun can be seen as a system.

A shadow is a 3–D area where light is blocked by an object.

The Moon's phases change from day to day in a cycle that lasts about a month.

Our changing view of sunlight shining on the Moon is what makes the Moon seem to change shape.

A solar eclipse occurs when the Moon blocks sunlight from reaching the Earth.

A lunar eclipse occurs when the Earth blocks sunlight from reaching the Moon.

2. **Some people still think that Moon phases are caused by Earth's shadow.** Say that some people who have seen this model still think that the phases of the Moon might be caused by Earth's shadow. They need even more evidence. Say that by closely observing shadows, students can gather more evidence that Moon phases are not caused by Earth's shadow on the Moon.

3. **Using shadows to predict object shapes.** Say that you are going to show them the shadows of some mystery objects. It is their job to try to figure out from the shadow what the *shape* of the object is—not what the object is, but its shape.

Be careful to place objects on the overhead projector very quietly, so that they don't make a telltale noise.

4. **Film canister on overhead.** Place the film canister upright on the overhead projector and turn the projector on. Based on the shadow, ask them what shape they think the object is. [Round.] Take a few responses, and then reorient the film canister on the projector so that they can see the shadow of its cylindrical shape. Finally, hold up the object so that they can see it.

5. **Ball on overhead.** Turn the projector off and set the ball (or marble) on the overhead, with a small piece of tape on the bottom to prevent it from rolling. Turn the projector back on, ask students to guess its shape, and then hold it up and reveal the object. Do the same with a coin, a cube, and a paper square.

6. **Difficult to determine shape from a shadow.** Conclude that it is hard to tell if something is flat or three-dimensional just by looking at the evidence of its shadow.

Using Shadows as Evidence for the Scientific Model

1. **Show the image of a crescent Moon.** Show the crescent moon on the top part of the overhead transparency or CD–ROM file: *Crescent and Quarter Moon Phases.* Ask, "From what we have just learned, could the Earth's shadow make the Moon look this shape?" [Yes, because the Earth's shadow is round, if it fell on the Moon it could look like this.] Admit that it is very understandable that some people think the Earth's shadow makes the Moon look this shape, but the next picture might change their minds.

TEACHER CONSIDERATIONS

PROVIDING MORE EXPERIENCE

More shadow objects: A possible extension or homework assignment could be for students to bring in a mystery object whose shape cannot be determined by its shadow. A student could put a mystery object on the projector and have classmates guess the shape.

CRESCENT AND QUARTER MOON PHASES

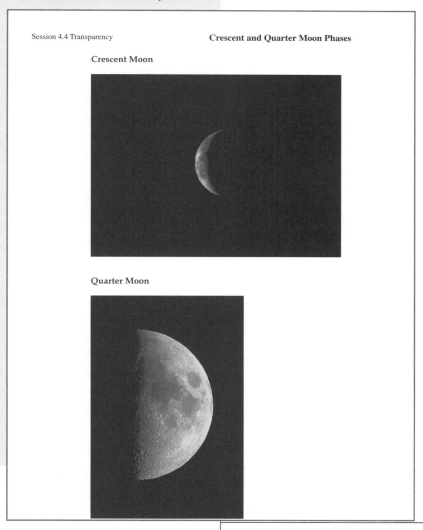

Session 4.4 Transparency

Crescent and Quarter Moon Phases

Crescent Moon

Quarter Moon

Unit Goals

The Earth and Moon move with regular and predictable motion.

The relationship between the Earth, Moon, and Sun can be seen as a system.

A shadow is a 3–D area where light is blocked by an object.

The Moon's phases change from day to day in a cycle that lasts about a month.

Our changing view of sunlight shining on the Moon is what makes the Moon seem to change shape.

A solar eclipse occurs when the Moon blocks sunlight from reaching the Earth.

A lunar eclipse occurs when the Earth blocks sunlight from reaching the Moon.

2. **It's not Earth's shadow.** Show the image of the quarter or "half" moon. Say that we see this shape of the Moon each month, too. Ask, "Could this shape of the Moon be caused by the Earth's shadow?" [No. The Earth is a ball, so its shadow would be curved, not straight like this.]

3. **Review what causes Moon phases.** Ask students to think back to the moon ball model and explain why the Moon sometimes looks like the half moon in the picture. [We see only the bright part of the Moon, and the brightness is caused by sunlight on the Moon. The dark part is the beginning of the Moon's shadow—the shadow on itself—the part that is not in the sunlight.]

4. **Scientific explanations are based on *all* the evidence.** Tell students that the scientific explanation for Moon phases is the one that fits *all* the evidence. Saying that the Earth's shadow causes Moon phases doesn't fit all the evidence.

Modeling an Eclipse of the Moon

1. **Distribute moon balls.** Say that they will get to use the moon ball model again, but this time they will use the moon balls to model something different. Remind students not to play with the moon balls.

2. **Gather around the light.** Gather the class in a circle around the light bulb, and hand out the moon balls. Illuminate the bulb, and turn off the room lights. Remind them that each of their heads represents the Earth, the light bulb represents the Sun, and the ball represents the Moon.

3. **Review Moon phases.** First, have students slowly turn to the left and model one cycle of moon phases.

4. **Stop at the full Moon phase.** Instruct your students to move their moon balls around again until they reach the full phase, with their backs to the light bulb. This time, have each student move the moon ball into the shadow of her head.

5. **Eclipse of the Moon/Lunar eclipse.** Explain that this is an *eclipse* of the Moon. It is sometimes called a *lunar eclipse.* Tell them that the word *eclipse* means "one object blocking the light from another." Ask, "What is blocking the light from falling on the moon ball?" [Their "Earth" heads.] Clarify that, unlike moon phases, lunar eclipses *are* caused by the Earth's shadow.

TEACHER CONSIDERATIONS

"Having talked about how shadows occur really gave the students enough evidence that what was occurring during eclipses was caused by shadows."

Unit Goals

The Earth and Moon move with regular and predictable motion.

The relationship between the Earth, Moon, and Sun can be seen as a system.

A shadow is a 3–D area where light is blocked by an object.

The Moon's phases change from day to day in a cycle that lasts about a month.

Our changing view of sunlight shining on the Moon is what makes the Moon seem to change shape.

A solar eclipse occurs when the Moon blocks sunlight from reaching the Earth.

A lunar eclipse occurs when the Earth blocks sunlight from reaching the Moon.

6. **Look at the edge of Earth's shadow on the Moon.** Ask each student to move the moon ball a little, so that he can see the edge of his head's shadow on the moon ball. Say that during a lunar eclipse, you can see the round edge of Earth's shadow move across the Moon.

7. **Lunar eclipses happen during the full Moon.** Ask, "Why does an eclipse of the Moon always happen during the full Moon?" [That's when the Earth is between the Sun and Moon, so that the Earth's shadow can fall on the Moon.]

8. **Why isn't there an eclipse every month?** Tell students that as the Moon orbits the Earth, it usually passes somewhere above or below the Earth's shadow, so, most of the time, we get a full Moon without an eclipse.

9. **Everyone on the night side of Earth sees the lunar eclipse.** While students continue to observe the eclipse of the Moon, point out that everyone who lives on the side of the Earth facing the Moon can see an eclipse of the Moon at the same time (weather permitting). Ask students to raise their hands if they have ever seen an eclipse of the Moon.

Modeling an Eclipse of the Sun

1. **Use moon balls to block the light bulb.** Now, ask your students to face the light bulb. Tell them to hold their moon balls directly between their heads and the light bulb. Ask what object is being blocked. [The Sun.] Ask what object is eclipsing the Sun. [The Moon.]

2. **Solar eclipse.** Say that when the Sun is blocked from our view, we call it a *solar eclipse*. Ask if anyone has ever seen a solar eclipse.

3. **Shadows on faces of classmates.** During the solar eclipse, have them glance around at other students' faces. Ask, "What is making the round shadows on everyone's faces?" [It's the shadow of the Moon.] Point out that not everybody on that side of Earth can see the solar eclipse: the Sun is blocked only for the people who live where that shadow is. (The people who live on your chin can still see the Sun!)

TEACHER CONSIDERATIONS

TEACHING NOTES

Short, straight hair helps: Students with short, straight hair will be better able to see the rounded shape of their heads than students with long, curly, or spiky hair. Remind students that the Earth has a relatively smooth, spherical shape.

Key Vocabulary

Science and Inquiry Vocabulary

Evidence

Scientific Explanation

Model

System

Prediction

Scientist

Scale Model

Three–Dimensional (3–D)

Two–Dimensional (2–D)

Space Science Vocabulary

Crescent Moon

Cycle

Diameter

Solar Eclipse (eclipse of the Sun)

Lunar Eclipse (eclipse of the Moon)

Full Moon

Gibbous

New Moon

Orbit

Phase

Quarter Moon

Satellite

Shadow

Sphere

Rotate

Revolve

4. Scientific model. Tell students that the model they have just used to explain eclipses is what scientists have found to be the best explanation. The model explains all the observations that people have made of eclipses, and there is no evidence against the model.

5. Collect materials. Turn on the lights, collect the moon balls, and have everyone return to their seats.

Photos of an Eclipse of the Sun

1. Show photos of an eclipse of the Sun. Show the *Eclipse of the Sun* images, and ask your students what they notice. Ask them to explain why we can't see the whole Sun in the picture. [The Moon is blocking the Sun from our view.] Remind them that, during an eclipse of the Sun, the Moon is between the Sun and Earth, and the Moon's shadow falls on part of the Earth.

2. Who has seen a solar eclipse? If any students in your class have seen an eclipse of the Sun, ask them to describe what it was like.

3. You need to be in the right place to see a solar eclipse. Remind them that when an eclipse of the Sun happens, not everyone on Earth can see it. You have to be on the part of Earth where the shadow of the Moon falls to see an eclipse of the Sun.

4. Post key concept. Add the following key concept to the concept wall:

> We see an eclipse of the Sun when the Moon goes in front of the Sun. This is called a solar eclipse.

Unit Goals

The Earth and Moon move with regular and predictable motion.

The relationship between the Earth, Moon, and Sun can be seen as a system.

A shadow is a 3–D area where light is blocked by an object.

The Moon's phases change from day to day in a cycle that lasts about a month.

Our changing view of sunlight shining on the Moon is what makes the Moon seem to change shape.

A solar eclipse occurs when the Moon blocks sunlight from reaching the Earth.

A lunar eclipse occurs when the Earth blocks sunlight from reaching the Moon.

ECLIPSE OF THE SUN

Session 4.4 Transparency

Eclipse of the Sun

Partial Solar Eclipse

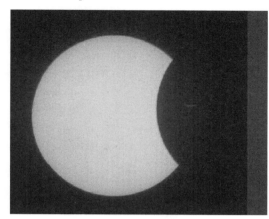

Total Solar Eclipse

Unit Goals

The Earth and Moon
move with regular and
predictable motion.

The relationship
between the Earth,
Moon, and Sun can
be seen as a system.

A shadow is a 3–D
area where light is
blocked by an object.

The Moon's phases
change from day to
day in a cycle that
lasts about a month.

Our changing view
of sunlight shining
on the Moon is what
makes the Moon seem
to change shape.

A solar eclipse occurs
when the Moon
blocks sunlight from
reaching the Earth.

A lunar eclipse occurs
when the Earth
blocks sunlight from
reaching the Moon.

Photos of an Eclipse of the Moon

1. **Show photos of eclipse of the Moon.** Show the *Eclipse of the Moon* image, and ask your students to explain why we can't see the whole Moon in the picture. [The Earth's shadow is falling on the Moon.] Point out the curved shape of the Earth's shadow in the photo.

2. **Image is fuzzy because of distance.** Ask why they think that the image looks fuzzy. Place a ball on the overhead projector, and slowly lift it. Point out that the shadow begins to look fuzzy with distance. Tell them that during a lunar eclipse, the Earth's shadow on the Moon also looks fuzzy, because the Earth is so far away from the Moon.

3. **Who has seen a lunar eclipse?** If any students in your class have seen a lunar eclipse, ask them to describe it.

4. **Eclipse of the Moon key concept.** Add the following key concept to the concept wall:

> We see an eclipse of the Moon when the Moon goes into the Earth's shadow. This is called a lunar eclipse.

TEACHER CONSIDERATIONS

ASSESSMENT OPPORTUNITY

Critical Juncture—Solar and Lunar Eclipses: If students have trouble identifying what is causing the eclipses pictured on the transparencies, consider providing more experience, as follows.

PROVIDING MORE EXPERIENCE

Pairs of students model eclipses with three spheres: Give each pair of students three balls to represent the Earth, Moon, and Sun. These could simply be balled-up pieces of aluminum foil or any small balls. Challenge them to work together to use the balls to model solar and lunar eclipses and explain to each other what is happening during each.

ECLIPSE OF THE MOON

Session 4.4 transparency

Eclipse of the Moon

Partial Lunar Eclipse

The idea for the eclipse pamphlet came from Sally Pellegrin who field tested Unit 4 with her fifth graders in Cleveland, Ohio.

Unit Goals

The Earth and Moon move with regular and predictable motion.

The relationship between the Earth, Moon, and Sun can be seen as a system.

A shadow is a 3–D area where light is blocked by an object.

The Moon's phases change from day to day in a cycle that lasts about a month.

Our changing view of sunlight shining on the Moon is what makes the Moon seem to change shape.

A solar eclipse occurs when the Moon blocks sunlight from reaching the Earth.

A lunar eclipse occurs when the Earth blocks sunlight from reaching the Moon.

An Eclipse Pamphlet

1. Making an eclipse pamphlet. Hold up an *Eclipse Pamphlet* student sheet. Say that to help students remember what causes these two different types of eclipses, they will complete the drawings on the sheet. Say that when they are finished, they will have made an educational pamphlet that they can use to show their friends or families what causes eclipses.

2. Fold the sheet. Give each student an *Eclipse Pamphlet* sheet, and tell them the printed side will be the "inside" of the pamphlet, where students will draw. Have them fold the edges of the sheet on the two dotted lines. (See illustration.)

3. Label the outside of the pamphlet with the words *Eclipses*, *Solar*, and *Lunar*. Show your sample pamphlet and have each student write the three labels and add their name to the outside of the pamphlet.

4. Explain the layout of the drawings. Have them open to the inside of the pamphlet again, and point out that there are two sections. In each section, the Sun and Earth are already pictured. The edge of the Sun is shown on the left. *Emphasize that the drawings are not to scale. The real Sun is much bigger and farther away from the Earth.*

5. Draw an eclipse of the Sun. On the left half of the page, students will draw the Moon where it would be during an eclipse of the Sun, and add shadows to the drawing. Remind them that the Moon is about one-fourth the size of the Earth.

6. Draw an eclipse of the Moon. Show them where they will do a drawing of an eclipse of the Moon (lunar eclipse) on the right half of the page. They will draw in the Moon and add shadows to the drawing.

7. Think about the moon ball model, and refer to the concept wall. To make their drawings, they should think back to the model they just did with the moon balls. Suggest that they also refer to the two key concepts about eclipses on the concept wall.

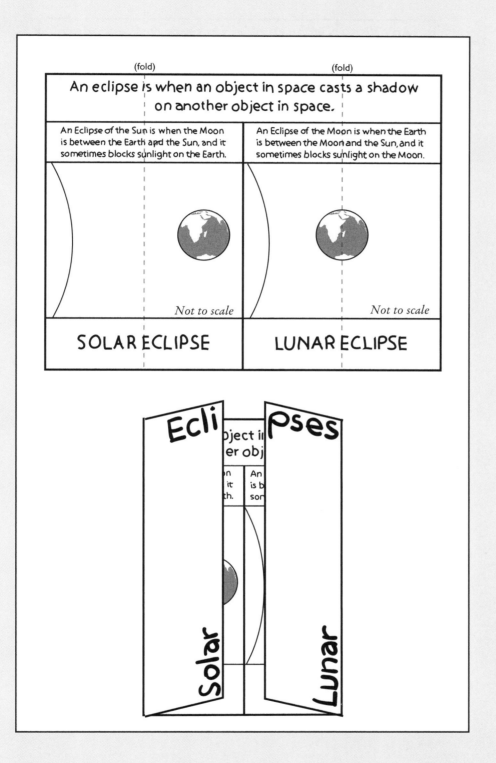

(fold)   (fold)

An eclipse is when an object in space casts a shadow on another object in space.

An Eclipse of the Sun is when the Moon is between the Earth and the Sun, and it sometimes blocks sunlight on the Earth.

An Eclipse of the Moon is when the Earth is between the Moon and the Sun, and it sometimes blocks sunlight on the Moon.

Not to scale

Not to scale

SOLAR ECLIPSE

LUNAR ECLIPSE

Eclipses

Solar

Lunar

Key Vocabulary

Science and Inquiry Vocabulary

Evidence

Scientific Explanation

Model

System

Prediction

Scientist

Scale Model

Three–Dimensional (3–D)

Two–Dimensional (2–D)

Space Science Vocabulary

Crescent Moon

Cycle

Diameter

Solar Eclipse (eclipse of the Sun)

Lunar Eclipse (eclipse of the Moon)

Full Moon

Gibbous

New Moon

Orbit

Phase

Quarter Moon

Satellite

Shadow

Sphere

Rotate

Revolve

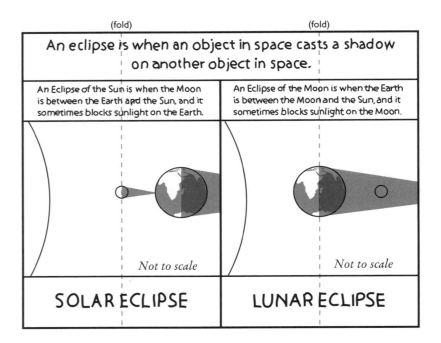

(fold)　　　　　　　　(fold)

An eclipse is when an object in space casts a shadow on another object in space.

An Eclipse of the Sun is when the Moon is between the Earth and the Sun, and it sometimes blocks sunlight on the Earth.

An Eclipse of the Moon is when the Earth is between the Moon and the Sun, and it sometimes blocks sunlight on the Moon.

Not to scale　　　*Not to scale*

SOLAR ECLIPSE　　**LUNAR ECLIPSE**

Unit Goals

The Earth and Moon move with regular and predictable motion.

The relationship between the Earth, Moon, and Sun can be seen as a system.

A shadow is a 3–D area where light is blocked by an object.

The Moon's phases change from day to day in a cycle that lasts about a month.

Our changing view of sunlight shining on the Moon is what makes the Moon seem to change shape.

A solar eclipse occurs when the Moon blocks sunlight from reaching the Earth.

A lunar eclipse occurs when the Earth blocks sunlight from reaching the Moon.

TEACHER CONSIDERATIONS

TEACHING NOTES

The pictures on page 478 show the positions and shadows for the two types of eclipses. *Please note: it is okay if students do not draw the shadow with the tapering shape shown here.* Because they have not made a complete study of light and shadow, students cannot be expected to know the shadow is shaped this way. The goal is for them to show the Moon in the Earth's shadow in a lunar eclipse, and to show the Moon's shadow cast on Earth during a solar eclipse.

ASSESSMENT OPPORTUNITY

Quick check for understanding: Their eclipse pamphlet drawings can serve as an assessment of students' understanding of the positions of the Sun, Earth, and Moon during lunar and solar eclipses. The drawings can also be used to assess whether students understand the role of shadows in eclipses.

QUESTIONNAIRE CONNECTION

Questionnaire questions #3 and #4 about eclipses are addressed by the activities in this session. In Session 4.5, students will have an opportunity to answer these questions again in the *Post–Unit 4 Questionnaire.*

Question #1 is also addressed by the eclipse pamphlet. As in question #1 and in *Shadow Play,* the pamphlet asks students to visualize the Sun's light on the Moon from an outside perspective. (In the moon ball activity, sunlight and shadow on the Moon are viewed from an Earth perspective.)

OPTIONAL PROMPT FOR WRITING OR DISCUSSION

You may want to have students use the prompt below for science journal writing at the end of this session or as homework.

- Which do you think would be more interesting to see: an eclipse of the Sun or an eclipse of the Moon? Why?

---

3. Why do we see an eclipse of the Sun? (Circle A, B, C, or D.) *Drawings are not to scale.*

A Clouds go in front of the Sun.	B The Moon goes between the Earth and the Sun.
Sun / Earth / (cloud)	Earth Moon Sun
C The Sun is between the Earth and the Moon.	D The Earth goes between the Moon and the Sun.
Earth Sun Moon	Moon Earth Sun

4. Why do we see an eclipse of the Moon? (Circle A, B, C, or D.) *Drawings are not to scale.*

A The Moon goes into the Earth's shadow.	B Clouds go in front of the Moon.
Moon Earth Sun	Moon Earth Sun
C The Moon goes between the Earth and the Sun.	D The Sun is between the Earth and the Moon.
Earth Moon Sun	Earth Sun Moon

1. Which picture below is *wrong*: A or B? (Circle one.) *Drawings are not to scale.*

It is wrong because. . . _____

_____

_____

_____

A	B
SUN MOON	SUN MOON

Unit Goals

The Earth and Moon move with regular and predictable motion.

The relationship between the Earth, Moon, and Sun can be seen as a system.

A shadow is a 3–D area where light is blocked by an object.

The Moon's phases change from day to day in a cycle that lasts about a month.

Our changing view of sunlight shining on the Moon is what makes the Moon seem to change shape.

A solar eclipse occurs when the Moon blocks sunlight from reaching the Earth.

A lunar eclipse occurs when the Earth blocks sunlight from reaching the Moon.

Overview

The session begins with a student reading—*Eclipse Chaser!* which reviews the concepts presented in Session 4.4. Then, in the *Impossible Missions* activity, the class encounters four humorous statements describing missions to the Moon and the Sun. Each statement contains inaccuracies that should be apparent to students who have a good grasp of the concepts addressed in Unit 4. Students work in evidence circles to discuss what's wrong with each statement and record their evidence-based explanations. At the end of Session 4.5, students fill out the *Post–Unit 4 Questionnaire* to assess how their ideas have changed.

This final session in the *Space Science Sequence* gives students a chance to review and apply concepts learned in Unit 4. Teachers whose classes have experienced more than one unit in the *Space Science Sequence* may select some of the *Additional Impossible Missions* to encourage students to revisit the concepts in other units of the sequence.

Impossible Missions	Estimated Time
Reading: *Eclipse Chaser!*	10 minutes
Impossible Missions	35 minutes
Post–Unit 4 Questionnaire	15 minutes
TOTAL	**60 minutes**

What You Need

For each student
- ❑ 1 copy of the reading *Eclipse Chaser!* from the student sheet packet
- ❑ *Impossible Missions* student sheet from the student sheet packet
- ❑ *Post–Unit 4 Questionnaire* from the student sheet packet
- ❑ pencil
- ❑ *optional: Additional Impossible Missions*, page 485

THE KEY CONCEPT WALL

BY THE END OF UNIT 4, YOUR CONCEPT WALL SHOULD LOOK SOMETHING LIKE THIS:

WHAT WE HAVE LEARNED ABOUT EVIDENCE AND MODELS

1. Evidence is information, such as measurements or observations, that is used to help explain things.

2. Scientists base their explanations on evidence.

3. Scientists question, discuss, and check each other's evidence and explanations.

4. Scientists use models to help understand and explain how things work.

5. Space scientists use models to study things that are very big or far away.

6. Models help us make and test predictions.

Note: These three concepts are not introduced in Units 2, 3, and 4. However, if you introduced them in Unit 1, keep them on the concept wall:

7. Every model is inaccurate in some way.

8. Models can be 3-dimensional or 2-dimensional.

9. A model can be an explanation in your mind.

WHAT WE HAVE LEARNED ABOUT SPACE SCIENCE

Unit 4: Moon Phases and Eclipses

4.1
A shadow is a dark area where light is blocked by an object.

Shadows are actually three dimensional.

We can see the shadow cast by one object on another object.

The shadow begins on the dark side of the object that is blocking the light.

4.2
The Moon can be seen sometimes at night and sometimes during the day.

The shape of the Moon as we see it changes from day to day in a cycle that lasts about a month.

The changes in the way the Moon looks are called phases.

Some of the Moon's phases are: new, crescent, quarter, gibbous, and full.

4.3
The Moon seems to change shape from day to day, but it is always round like a sphere.

It takes the Moon about a month to orbit the Earth once.

Phases of the Moon are not caused by Earth's shadow.

Our changing view of sunlight shining on the Moon is what makes the Moon seem to change shape.

The Sun, Earth, and Moon form a system.

4.4
We see an eclipse of the Sun when the Moon goes in front of the Sun. This is called a solar eclipse.

We see an eclipse of the Moon when the Moon goes into the Earth's shadow. This is called a lunar eclipse.

ECLIPSE CHASER! PAGE 1

Session 4.5 Reading, page 1

Eclipse Chaser!

My name is Isabel, and I am a space scientist. My job is studying space. Even when I am not at work, one of my favorite things is chasing and watching eclipses. You don't have to travel to another place to see lunar eclipses when they happen, but to see a solar eclipse, you have to be in the right place at the right time. Eclipse chasers find out when and where solar eclipses are going to happen, and travel to see them as often as they can.

Isabel Hawkins talks to television reporters just before a total solar eclipse in Turkey.

During an eclipse of the Moon, you get to see Earth's shadow on the Moon! When I watch a lunar eclipse, I can really picture myself on a big, round planet orbiting the Sun, with one Moon orbiting us. But solar eclipses are what I really love. There is nothing in the world like a total solar eclipse!

When a solar eclipse begins, the Moon just blocks the edge of the Sun. Slowly, the daylight gets dim and gray. Shadows look different in this light. It takes about 1 hour and 15 minutes for the Moon to block the Sun completely.

Just before the Moon completely covers the Sun, things start happening fast. You can see the gigantic shadow of the Moon moving across the ground toward you at more than a thousand miles per hour. It's almost scary, because the shadow is moving so fast. When the shadow reaches you, the Moon is completely blocking the Sun where you are standing.

One moment before the Moon completely blocks the Sun, you see the "diamond ring." People observe it with cameras and special eye protection. The Sun's light around the dark Moon looks like a giant diamond ring in the sky. That's when people start screaming and shouting with excitement.

Looking at the Sun at any time without special protection can harm your eyes. The same is true before and after the total eclipse. The only time it's safe to watch the eclipse without eye protection is when the Sun is completely blocked.

When the Moon blocks the Sun completely, the day suddenly becomes dark and cold. Animals get confused. Cows and birds will head home the way they do at sunset. Looking up at the total eclipse feels strange and beautiful. You can see what look like red flames reaching out from the Sun. In the dark sky you can see some stars and planets.

In just a few minutes, the Sun peeks out from the other side of the Moon. That's the second time you get to see the "diamond ring." Then everything that happened at the beginning of the eclipse happens again, in reverse. Eventually, the Moon is blocking only one edge of the Sun. Finally, the Moon moves away from the Sun, and it's bright daylight again.

We don't have total solar eclipses near us very often. It may take a long trip to see one, but I think they are totally worth it. I just returned from a trip to Turkey to see one. I hope to see many more!

Getting Ready

1. Make a copy of the *Eclipse Chaser!* reading, the *Impossible Missions* student sheet, and the *Post–Unit 4 Questionnaire* for each student.

2. Decide if you will use any of the *Additional Impossible Missions* for review of concepts in earlier units.

Reading: *Eclipse Chaser!*

1. Eclipse chasers travel to see total solar eclipses. Tell them that some people travel long distances to see a total eclipse of the Sun. Let them know that they'll now read about an eclipse chaser.

2. Read and discuss. Have students read *Eclipse Chaser!* and ask them a few questions, such as "What do you think it would be like during a total solar eclipse?" "Which would you rather see, a lunar or a solar eclipse? Why?"

3. Briefly review the causes of eclipses. Ask, "Why do eclipse chasers often have to travel to see a full eclipse?" [The Moon's shadow passes over only part of the Earth.]

Impossible Missions to the Moon and Sun

1. Evidence circles. Tell the class that they will work in evidence circles of four students to discuss some "impossible" missions to the Moon and Sun. Tell them that, because they understand the scientific model of how the Earth–Moon–Sun system works, they will probably notice that these missions don't make much sense.

TEACHER CONSIDERATIONS

TEACHING NOTES

Reading level: The reading level of page 1 of the reading is appropriate for most third and fourth graders. Page 2 and the additional pages on the CD-ROM are for students who are interested in further information on the topic, and who are able to read at a slightly higher level.

Session 4.5 Reading, page 2   **An Interview with Isabel Hawkins**

Question: What do you study in space?

Isabel: I started out studying the stuff that is between the stars in space. I also study stars, like the Sun. Now, I share space science discoveries with people who are not scientists.

Question: What made you decide to be a space scientist?

Isabel: When I was 10 years old in Argentina, a book salesman came to our house. He sold us a book on the solar system. I looked at the amazing pictures of the planets, and I was hooked! Ever since then, I knew I wanted to be a space scientist.

Question: What other interests do you have?

Isabel: When I was young, I played on a volleyball team and I liked nice clothes. Today I like cooking, kickboxing, and golf. And I like chasing eclipses!

Question: What made you move to the United States?

Isabel: When I was 16, I came to the United States as an exchange student for one year. I later returned to the United States and studied at a university. After nine years in university studies, I began working as a space scientist for NASA and the University of California at Berkeley.

Question: What does it feel like when it gets dark in the middle of the day during a total eclipse?

Isabel: The whole experience is very moving, It brings tears to my eyes.

More About Solar Eclipses

Eclipses happen when a star does interesting things with a planet and a moon. Our nearest star is the Sun, our nearest planet is the Earth (we're on it), and our nearest moon is what we call "the Moon." The Moon orbits the Earth, and the Earth orbits the Sun. Because of these movements, sometimes the Sun's light is blocked on either the Earth or the Moon. We call these solar or lunar eclipses.

Solar Eclipses: Once a month, during the new moon, the Moon is between the Earth and the Sun. The Moon is usually too high or too low in its orbit to block the light of the Sun from reaching part of Earth. But sometimes the Moon orbits in the exact right position to block the Sun. The Moon is about 400 times smaller than the Sun, but it is also about 400 times closer to Earth than the Sun is. Even though the Sun is so much bigger than the Moon, it looks much smaller than it really is because it is so much farther away than the Moon. From Earth, the Moon and Sun look like they are about the same size. The Moon is just barely big enough to block the Sun completely. Sometimes the Moon isn't in the perfect position, and it only blocks part of the Sun. We call that a partial solar eclipse. When the Moon blocks the whole Sun, that's called a total solar eclipse. The shadow of the Moon is small, about 160 miles in diameter. During a total solar eclipse, the Moon's shadow is a dot 160 miles in diameter that moves across the daylight side of the Earth. If you are not in the right spot on the Earth, the shadow doesn't hit you, and you don't see the eclipse. A solar eclipse can last a few hours, but the part when the Sun is totally blocked lasts only a few minutes. The longest time the Sun is ever totally blocked is about seven and a half minutes.

How often do eclipses happen? From the time when you are born to the time you finish high school, there will be about 29 lunar eclipses. There will be about 31 partial solar eclipses, but only 10 total solar eclipses.

What Causes the "Diamond Ring?" Usually, you can't see the Sun's outer atmosphere, because the Sun is too bright. But during a solar eclipse, the Moon blocks the Sun's bright rays. That's when you can see the Sun's atmosphere glowing like a golden ring around the round Moon. That is the ring part of what is called the diamond ring. The diamond in the ring is the last flash of sunlight shining through a valley on the edge of the Moon. Isabel says it's much more beautiful than any diamond ring that you can put on your finger.

IMPOSSIBLE MISSIONS

Session 4.5 Student Sheet

Name _____

Four Impossible Missions to the Moon and Sun

Whoever designed the four missions below does not understand Moon phases or eclipses. Write on the lines below what is wrong with each mission, and explain why it is wrong. There may be more than one thing wrong with each mission.

1. Our mission is to land on the Moon. We can't land during the new moon, because that's when the Moon is gone.

_____

_____

_____

2. If we land when it is a crescent moon, we can explore the Moon very quickly, because it will be so small.

_____

_____

_____

3. Each day while exploring on the Moon, we will pass into the Earth's shadow, and it will be night.

_____

_____

_____

4. We will land on the Sun during an eclipse of the Sun, so it won't be so hot there.

_____

_____

_____

2. Explain what's wrong with each mission. Say that each of the missions has at least one thing wrong with it. Your students' job will be to discuss within their evidence circles what's wrong with each one, and why it is wrong.

3. Review the procedure for evidence circles. Say that there are four *Impossible Missions*, and that each student will get a chance to read one aloud. After each statement is read, all students on the team will get a turn to explain what is wrong with the mission and why. To do this, they should use the scientific evidence they have gathered about phases of the Moon and eclipses. Tell them that after their team has discussed what is wrong with the mission, each student will write their explanations and evidence on their data sheet.

4. Pass out an *Impossible Missions* sheet to each student. Depending on your students, you may want to discuss one of the missions together as a whole class for practice.

1. Our mission is to land on the Moon. We can't land during the new moon, because that's when the Moon is gone.

2. If we land when it is a crescent moon, we can explore the Moon very quickly, because it will be so small.

3. Each day while exploring on the Moon, we will pass into the Earth's shadow, and it will be night.

4. We will land on the Sun during an eclipse of the Sun, so it won't be so hot there.

TEACHER CONSIDERATIONS

ADDITIONAL IMPOSSIBLE MISSIONS (ORGANIZED BY UNIT)

Unit 1
- Because the Moon is so close, we should be able to make the trip in a few hours.
- We will have to be careful that we don't mix up the Moon and the Sun. Because they are about the same size, it is easy to get them mixed up.
- Because the Moon is farther away than the Sun, we may stop to camp on the Sun, and then later go on to the Moon.
- It will probably take us a whole day to get to the Sun.
- After we land on the Sun, we will explore the whole Sun in our solar car. This should take about one week.
- On a mission to the stars, we may go to Mars, too, because it's just about the same distance away from us as the stars are.

Unit 2
- We will take off from Earth at night, because there is less gravity then.
- For a soft landing, we will use parachutes to land on the Moon.
- When we get out of our spaceship on the Moon, we will be able to fly around, because there is no gravity there.
- When we arrive on the Moon, we will be able to take off our helmets and breathe the air on the Moon.
- We will leave a flag there and take pictures of it flapping in the wind.
- Taking off from the Moon to return home will be easy, because there is no gravity on the Moon.
- When returning to Earth, we will need to make sure that we land on the flat part of the top of the Earth, so we do not fall off.
- It may be hard to get our spacecraft to land back on the Earth, because gravity may push us away from it.

Unit 3
- We will go to the Moon at night, because that is when the Moon is out.
- We will use a big balloon to escape the pull of Earth's gravity, and take us all the way to the Moon.
- We will go to the Sun at night, so we can land while it is dark and not hot.
- We will need to time our flight to the Sun carefully, because the Sun is always traveling around the Earth. The Sun takes about one month to travel around the Earth.
- When returning to Earth, we will need to time it so we don't land when the Moon's shadow is causing night on Earth.

Unit 4
- If we land when the Moon is full, it will take a long time to explore, because it will be bigger than Earth.
- If we land on the dark part of the Moon, we will need to wait until Earth's shadow moves away before we can explore.

Key Vocabulary

Evidence

Scientific Explanation

Model

System

Prediction

Scientist

Scale Model

Three–Dimensional (3–D)

Two–Dimensional (2–D)

Crescent Moon

Cycle

Diameter

Solar Eclipse (eclipse of the Sun)

Lunar Eclipse (eclipse of the Moon)

Full Moon

Gibbous

New Moon

Orbit

Phase

Quarter Moon

Satellite

Shadow

Sphere

Rotate

Revolve

Unit Goals

The Earth and Moon move with regular and predictable motion.

The relationship between the Earth, Moon, and Sun can be seen as a system.

A shadow is a 3–D area where light is blocked by an object.

The Moon's phases change from day to day in a cycle that lasts about a month.

Our changing view of sunlight shining on the Moon is what makes the Moon seem to change shape.

A solar eclipse occurs when the Moon blocks sunlight from reaching the Earth.

A lunar eclipse occurs when the Earth blocks sunlight from reaching the Moon.

5. **Whole-class sharing.** When students have finished their discussions, and have written their explanations on the *Impossible Missions* student sheet, take a few minutes with the whole class for students to share what is wrong with these missions and why. Students may say:

1. "The Moon is always there. The reason that we can't see the new moon is that we are looking at the side that is in shadow. That part of the Moon is dark, so we can't see it."

2. "The Moon doesn't change size. When we see a crescent moon, we are seeing the part of the Moon that is lit by the Sun. The rest of the Moon is still there, but we can't see it because it is in shadow."

3. "The Earth's shadow does not fall on the Moon each day (although it does fall on the Moon occasionally during eclipses of the Moon). While we are exploring the Moon, we might pass into shadow, but that shadow is the shadow of the Moon on itself."

4. "The Sun doesn't get cooler during an eclipse. During an eclipse of the Sun, the Moon blocks the Sun's light from our view. The Sun remains as hot as ever."

6. *Optional:* **Analyze additional "Impossible Missions."** Depending on the time available and how many other units in the *Space Science Sequence* your students have experienced, use as many as you can of the other missions listed at the end of this session to review the concepts that students have learned. These *Additional Impossible Missions* are organized by unit; select the ones that you think are most appropriate for your class. Students can use the back of their sheet or additional paper to write their responses.

7. **Congratulate students on their ability to apply the important space science ideas that they have been learning to these different mission ideas.**

TEACHER CONSIDERATIONS

OPTIONAL PROMPTS FOR WRITING OR DISCUSSION

You may want to have students use the prompts below for science journal writing at the end of this session or as homework. The prompts could also be used for a discussion or during a final student sharing circle.

- Many of the ways that we mark time are based on the movements of the Earth, Moon and Sun. Describe what space object's movement marks the length of:
  - a day
  - a month
  - a year

- If the Earth had no Moon, would any of these still happen? Why or why not?
  - eclipse of the Moon
  - eclipse of the Sun
  - full Moon

- If the Earth had two Moons, how do you think these might change:
  - eclipses of the Moon
  - eclipses of the Sun
  - Moon phases

POST–UNIT 4 QUESTIONNAIRE, PAGE 1

Session 4.5

Name_____

Post–Unit 4 Questionnaire, page 1

1. Why do we see an eclipse of the Moon? (Circle A, B, C, or D.) *Drawings are not to scale.*

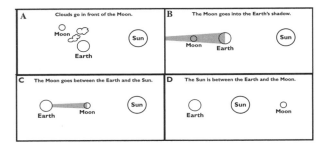

2. Here are some pictures of how the Moon looks at different times of the month.

Why does the Moon seem to change its shape during the month? (Circle A, B, C, or D.)
A. The Earth's shadow covers part of the Moon.
B. We see the sunny side of the Moon from different directions.
C. The Moon gets smaller and bigger.
D. Clouds block part of the Moon from our view.

(Over)

The *Post–Unit 4 Questionnaire*

1. Find out how their ideas have changed. Tell your class that they have learned a lot since they took the *Pre–Unit 4 Questionnaire.* Let them know that they will now get a chance to take it again, to see how their ideas about phases and eclipses have changed. Remind them that the ability to change one's ideas based on evidence is a sign of being a good scientist.

2. Work independently. Once again, say that the questionnaire is designed to find out what *each* student is thinking, and caution students not to help one another.

3. Distribute pencils and questionnaires. Give students a task to do if they finish early, so that everyone else has a chance to finish the questionnaire.

TEACHER CONSIDERATIONS

PROVIDING MORE EXPERIENCE

Design a Spaceship to Go to the Moon: For an additional opportunity to apply concepts from all four units of the *Space Science Sequence*, assign teams of students to design a "possible" spaceship to travel to the Moon.

1. Plan a space mission that really could happen. Plan a mission that *is* possible, to the only place other than Earth where humans have ever walked: the Moon.

2. Be sure to include what you know about gravity, air, size, distance, etc. Make a drawing together with your team, but each person must turn in a sheet with these questions answered:

- How will your spaceship escape the Earth's gravity?
- How big will it be? Why? How much will it weigh? Why?
- Will there be windows on the spaceship? What kind? Will the astronauts be able to open them?
- How will your spaceship land on the Moon? Why?
- What will your astronauts need to wear when they leave the spaceship to explore the Moon? Why?
- How will you keep your flag open on the Moon?
- How will your spaceship land back on Earth? Why?
- Draw the Moon and Earth, and draw a line showing the whole trip of where your space ship will be going.
- How many total kilometers will you be traveling?

Session 4.5

Name_____

Post–Unit 4 Questionnaire, page 2

3. Why do we see an eclipse of the Sun? (Circle A, B, C, or D). *Drawings are not to scale.*

A The Moon goes between the Earth and the Sun.	B Clouds go in front of the Sun.
Earth Moon Sun	Earth Sun
C The Earth goes between the Moon and the Sun.	D The Sun is between the Earth and the Moon.
Moon Earth Sun	Earth Sun Moon

4. Which picture below is *wrong*: A or B? (Circle one.) *Drawings are not to scale.*

It is wrong because. . . _____

_____

_____

A SUN MOON   B SUN MOON